SCHOOLS COUNCIL

MODULAR COURSES IN TECHNOLOGY

ELECTRONICS

Paul Fay

Roy Pickup

Clive Braithwaite

Jeffrey Hall

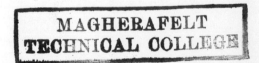
Oliver & Boyd

in association with the National Centre for School Technology

PROJECT TEAM

Director
Dr Ray Page

Co-ordinators
Roy Pickup
John Poole

Jeffrey Hall
Dr Duncan Harris
John Hucker
Michael Ives
Peter Patient

Oliver & Boyd
Robert Stevenson House
1–3 Baxter's Place
Leith Walk
Edinburgh EH1 3BB

A Division of Longman Group Ltd

ISBN 0 05 003383 2

First published 1980
Third impression 1982

Printed in Hong Kong by
Commonwealth Printing Press Ltd

Contents

Acknowledgments

For permission to reproduce certain photographs in this book, the authors and publishers would like to thank the following:

The Science Museum (Fig 1);
Mullard Limited (Figs 2, 4, 5, 12.2, 12.3, 12.4);
The Post Office (Fig 6);
Texas Instruments Limited (Fig 7);
RS Components Limited (Figs 4.34c, 5.17, 6.6, 6.7, 7.17);
Avo Limited, Dover, England (Fig 5.8);
Jackson Brothers (London) Limited (Fig 10.16);
International Computers Limited (Figs 12.1, 12.5, 12.6, 12.7).

Note The sign ■ has been used in the text to signify material suitable for both O-level and CSE candidates. The sign ☐ indicates material required only for the O-level examination.

Introduction

The Impact of Electronics in Industry and Society

Electronics play an increasingly greater role in our everyday life. Scientists and engineers probe the ocean depths, monitor the behaviour of the human body, and venture into the far reaches of space with tools and devices made available by electronics. Many household appliances, such as radio and television sets, the telephone, automatic tea-makers and adjustable-speed hand tools, owe their existence to electronic circuits; and electronic control of manufacturing processes by computers is becoming more commonplace.

The Development of Electronics

Before looking at the present-day situation, it is interesting to follow the developments in electronics from the end of the last century. In these early days, up to the start of the First World War, the effort was concentrated on the development of electrical systems of communication. It was during this period that Marconi and his colleagues demonstrated that two-way communication was possible using 'radio transmission and reception'. In the early days of marine radio communication, there were many dramatic incidents which emphasised the importance of this new communication medium. Perhaps the most interesting story relates to the arrest of the murderer Dr Crippen in 1910, when the captain of an ocean-going liner was able to use the ship's wireless installation to summon the help of Scotland Yard. Another story describes the sinking, with the loss of 1500 lives, of the liner *Titanic* in 1912. Radio communication was used for three days and nights following the receipt of the first startling message, which read:

'SS TITANIC RAN INTO ICEBERG. SINKING FAST'.

It was the loss of the *Titanic*, and the great service which radio had performed, that aroused public awareness to the need for this new means of communication. In fact, during the First World War, several laws were introduced which laid down that British ships above a certain size, and carrying more than a certain number of people, must carry a suitable wireless installation.

During the period between the two World Wars, as well as the further development of commercial communication systems taking place, a lot of industrial effort was aimed at the entertainment market. The British Broadcasting Company had started broadcasts in 1922. At the start of the Second

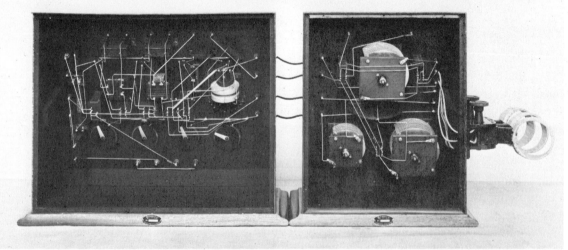

Fig 1   Four-valve broadcast receiver built in 1923 (front and rear views)

World War, audio broadcasting was well-established on the long, medium and short wavebands, and the first television programmes had been transmitted. Fig 1 shows the front and rear views of a four-valve audio broadcast receiver built in 1923. It is interesting to compare the constructional techniques used with those in present-day electronic equipment.

The development of commercial communication systems had resulted in the fitting of equipment aboard ships and aircraft, which enabled them to communicate with other stations on a world-wide network. The use of radio navigation equipment was well established by the end of the Second World War. The most important system of radio navigation worked on the principle of finding the direction of a radio signal using 'direction finding' aerials and equipment.

The Second World War brought increased activity in research and development in the electronics industry. This was necessary because of the requirement for more sophisticated equipment and the need to be in advance of the enemy where military equipment was concerned. Many of the electronic systems in use today had forerunners which were developed in wartime.

The period from the end of the Second World War has been marked by several major and interesting developments and electronics is now 'big business'. The methods of constructing components and equipment have changed many times. Interconnection of components is not limited to the use of the simple soldered joint. Electron and laserbeam welding may be used, or a thermo-compression or wrapped joint may be made. Point-to-point wiring and connection systems are being replaced by printed wiring boards, which may be multilayer in construction to cater for the increased complexity of connections and the miniaturised construction of components. Fig 2 shows two printed circuit wiring boards which, because of their rigid construction, can also dispense with the 'chassis' type circuit assemblies.

Fig 2   Printed circuit wiring boards

The components used in electronic circuits have also gone through many constructional changes, due mainly to the progress towards 'microminiaturisation' that has occurred. In the early 1960's the 'integrated electronic circuit' was introduced. This type of circuit is called an 'integrated circuit' in order to compare it with the conventional 'discrete' component circuit, which is made up of transistors, diodes, resistors and capacitors. An integrated circuit consists of a tiny wafer of semiconducting material (silicon), which is exposed to various chemicals in the vapour phase. These diffuse into the wafer to produce the four basic electronic components – resistors, capacitors, diodes and transistors. Combinations of these four components are then made to give the required electronic circuit function. The final integrated circuit is extremely small and an idea of the size can be gained by studying Fig 3, which shows the relative dimensions of the wafer, the circuit and the component.

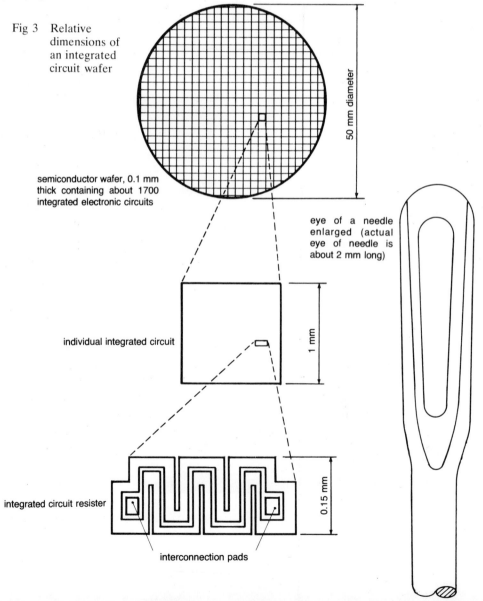

Fig 3   Relative dimensions of an integrated circuit wafer

50 mm diameter

semiconductor wafer, 0.1 mm thick containing about 1700 integrated electronic circuits

eye of a needle enlarged (actual eye of needle is about 2 mm long)

individual integrated circuit

1 mm

integrated circuit resister

0.15 mm

interconnection pads

Fig 4   Integrated circuits for use in electronic organs

Fig 5 (*below*)   Large-scale integrated circuits

After the diffusion and interconnection of the individual components has been completed, the wafer is 'scribed' between the circuits to leave 'dice' approximately 1 mm square. The dice are then mounted in standard packages similar to those shown in Figs 4 and 5. Each of the 'dual-in-line' packages shown in Fig 4 contains seven electronic circuits, which can be used to produce seven notes in an electronic organ.

The Present Day

Some of the early pioneers in electronics would be surprised, if they returned today, to see the range of applications for electronic devices and equipment. There is hardly an area of present-day human activity that does not depend, in some way or another, on the use of electronics. It will help us to understand how dependent modern society is on electronics if we look at a few of the modern systems in the main areas of use. It is a feature of modern civilisation that people should be able to speak to other people over short and long distances; machines such as computers must communicate via data transmission links; and television pictures must be transmitted between continents and lunar space vehicles. These can all be 'fixed' electronic communication systems. One of the latest developments in fixed communication equipment

Fig 6   PO Ground Station, Madely, Herefordshire

is the use of communication satellites which are placed in orbit, about 22 000 miles above the Earth's surface, to relay telephone and television signals over a world-wide network. These satellite signals are transmitted from Earth using 'parabolic reflector' type stations similar to that shown in Fig 6.

In the field of mobile communications, ships also have satellite communication and navigation systems which have been designed to provide communication on a 24-hour basis. Telephone conversations between ships and shore have been a feature for many years. Did you know you can have a copy of the *Daily Telegraph* whilst having breakfast at sea aboard the *QE2*? This 8-page mini-paper contains all the latest news, not to mention the advertisements and famous crossword puzzle. The paper is produced with the help of electronics.

The performance of computers is improving steadily and the size and cost of systems is being reduced yearly. Much of the present-day success in the computer industry has been due to the dramatic advances made in microelectronic (integrated circuit) systems. The use of microcomputers is opening up new realms of computer applications. This type of computer depends for its operation on a complex integrated circuit chip, called a microprocessor, which is about 10 mm square in size and may contain five or six thousand transistors. These microcomputers are used for such purposes as electronic scales and sales terminals (now common in supermarkets), traffic-light control systems, etc. The next stage down from the microcomputer is, of course, the hand-held calculator which again depends for its operation on an integrated circuit. Not so many years ago, a calculator, which would do the same calculations as the hand-held type shown in Fig 7, would have been the size of a suitcase.

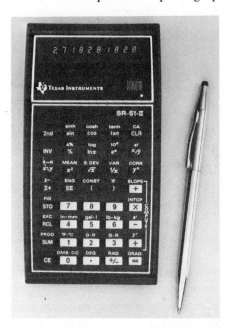

Fig 7   Hand-held electronic calculator

Looking at the advances in medicine that have been made possible by the use of electronics, there can be no question of its value. The treatment of major heart defects could not proceed without the measurements and, in some cases, temporary life-support systems available through the use of electronics. The impact of electronics has been to provide a general improvement in the precision of medical measurements and, due to the miniaturisation of electronic components, to allow measurements to be made inside the body. The replacement of certain body functions can also be achieved, examples being the heart 'pacemaker' and the kidney machine.

This introduction has given a brief insight into the development of electronics up to the present day. New developments are constantly taking place in this very rapidly expanding field. Very few years ago, the idea of computers in the home would have been thought out of the question, but with recent advances they are beginning to become a reality. Electronics is an ever-advancing area of technology and who is to say what is going to happen in the future.

1 Simple Circuits

■ Introduction

The study of electronics is concerned with the behaviour of charged particles, called electrons, in solids, gases and vacuums. In this module, we will be concerned with a simple understanding of how electrons move in conducting and semi-conducting materials, and the elementary uses of electronic devices such as transistors. We shall look at the functions electronic devices can perform and their applications in simple systems. This course will not enable you to answer questions such as 'What is electricity?' or 'What does the electron look like?'. We are not able to directly see electrons because of their small size, but you will be able to observe the result of electrons moving round a circuit by the effect they have on a meter, or the effect that a beam of electrons has in moving across the screen of a cathode-ray oscilloscope or scanning the tube face of your television.

■ Electrons and Electricity

All matter in the universe is made up of **atoms**. An atom consists of a **nucleus** of **protons** and other particles (neutrons) around which orbit **electrons**. Due to arbitrary choice by early physicists, the **electric charge** on an electron was said to be **negative** (−ve) and the charge on a proton was said to be **positive** (+ve).

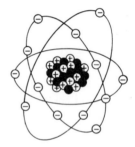

Fig 1.1   The structure of an atom

In **conducting materials** such as copper, silver and brass, some of the outer electrons of the atoms can move freely through the atomic structure when an electrical pressure is applied to the conductor. This movement is called an **electric current**.

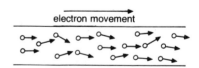

Fig 1.2   Electric current is the movement of electrons

Electrons cannot move through the atomic structure of **insulating materials** such as rubber, PVC and mica. The study of the behaviour and control of electrons in materials is called **electronics**.

Since we cannot cut open a conductor and see the electrons moving, we need to be able to use a model so that we can understand more clearly what is happening. The flow of water in a pipe behaves in a very similar manner to the flow of electricity in a conductor. We will use the water flow process as an analogy to help us understand the flow of electrons.

■ Water Flow Analogy

Making a comparison between ideas or concepts, to help understand what is happening, is called making an 'analogy'. We can use the analogy of water flow in a pipe to help us understand the movement of electrons in a wire. The larger the diameter of a water pipe, the more water can flow through the pipe in a given time.

Fig 1.3 shows a water container with both a narrow and a wide pipe outlet. There is a larger flow of water from the wide pipe than from the narrow pipe in a given time.

Fig 1.4 uses the water analogy to compare the movement of electrons in two wires with the flow of water in two pipes. There is a larger current of water flowing in the large diameter pipe than in the small diameter pipe. A large diameter wire or conductor carries a larger current (or flow of electrons) than a small diameter wire.

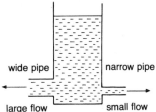

Fig 1.3   Water flow in wide and narrow pipes

Fig 1.4   Water flow in a pipe and electron flow in a conductor

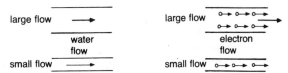

1   *What will happen if two pipes are placed side by side, replacing one pipe of the same diameter?*

The movement or flow of water is called the current. The water shown in Fig 1.5 will flow in the direction indicated by the arrow because of the **pressure difference** produced by the difference in levels of the water in the left- and right-hand containers.

The water will continue to flow until the water levels in the two containers are the same (i.e. until there is no pressure difference).

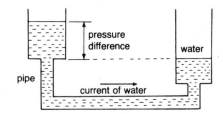

Fig 1.5   Water flow – current caused by pressure difference

2 Complete the statement: 'In order for a current to flow there must be a . . .'

In Fig 1.6 a pump has been added so that the water continues to flow. The pump maintains the pressure difference.

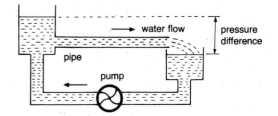

Fig 1.6   Complete water circuit

3 If the pump sets up a greater pressure difference, how will this affect the flow?

4 How will the diameter of the pipe affect the flow?

The rate of flow of water in a pipe depends on the pressure difference applied to the pipe.

Look at Fig 1.7*a*. Can you see how the rate of water flow out of the tank will be affected as the water level falls from level 1 to level 5? The rate of flow of water will decrease as the level falls, since the pressure on the water in the pipe drops. This could be illustrated by the diagram in Fig 1.7*b*.

Fig 1.7 (a)   Water levels in a tank cause pressure differences

It is the pressure difference caused by different levels of water in a tank that determines the rate at which the water empties from a tank. A large pressure difference causes a large flow rate of water and a small pressure difference causes a small flow rate of water. See Fig 1.7*c*.

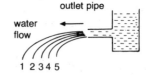

(b)   Decreasing rates of flow of water from a tank outlet pipe

We can use the water analogy to explain voltage in an electrical circuit. In electrical circuits, pressure difference is called **voltage**. A large voltage applied across a conducting wire causes a large flow of electrons (or large current) and a small voltage applied across a conductor causes a small current to flow. See Fig 1.8.

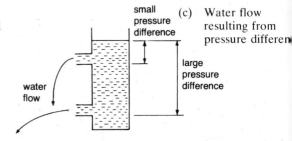

(c)   Water flow resulting from pressure differen[ce]

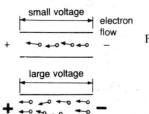

Fig 1.8   Small voltage causes small current, large voltage causes large current

14

We will return to this idea of water flow on several occasions throughout the course, drawing an analogy between water flow and flow of electricity, as it is such a useful method of understanding what is happening.

■ Flow of Electricity

Pressure difference across an electrical conductor is called voltage. In an electrical circuit, the device that maintains the electrical pressure difference is called a **cell** or battery.

The basic storage unit that can provide a pressure difference or voltage in an electrical circuit is called a cell.

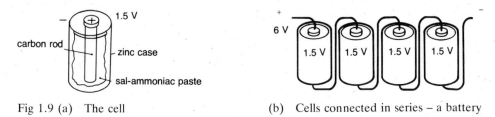

Fig 1.9 (a)   The cell   (b)   Cells connected in series – a battery

A collection of cells wired together in series is called a **battery** of cells. The electrical symbols for the cell and the battery are shown in Fig 1.10*a* and *b*.

Fig 1.10 (a)   Symbol for cell   (b)   Symbol for battery

The high electrical pressure side of a battery is called the **positive terminal** (marked + or coloured red).

The low electrical pressure side of a battery is called the **negative terminal** (marked − or coloured black).

Note These terminals must be connected correctly when the battery is used.

The property of a conductor that controls how much current flows is called **resistance**. The larger the resistance of a conductor the less the current that can flow, and the smaller the resistance the more current can flow when a given voltage is applied across the conductor.

The direction of **conventional current** flow from positive (+ve) to negative (−ve) was decided by early physicists in the nineteenth century. The discovery, in the early twentieth century, of electric current due to electron motion proved that electrons flow from negative (−ve) to positive (+ve). The movement of electrons is in fact in the opposite direction to the conventional current. We will return to this later in the course.

■ Electrical Diagrams

There are several ways of representing the electrical circuits that correspond to the water flow diagrams of Fig 1.6. The simplest way of detecting a flow of electricity is to use a lightbulb and the symbol for this is shown in Fig 1.11.

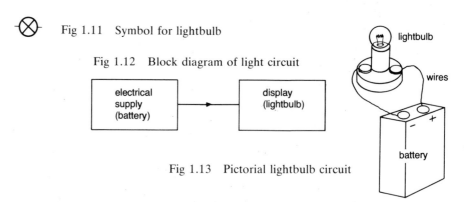

Fig 1.11   Symbol for lightbulb

Fig 1.12   Block diagram of light circuit

Fig 1.13   Pictorial lightbulb circuit

Fig 1.12 shows a simple block diagram. You will find this method used frequently in this course, particularly for design problems. Fig 1.13 shows a pictorial representation of the simple circuit with a battery and lightbulb.

Figs 1.14*a* and *b* show two wiring layouts of the **circuit diagram** that correspond to the water flow circuit of Fig 1.6. Fig 1.14*c* shows the method of translating this diagram into an electronic circuit diagram. The battery is not shown in the electronic circuit diagram, but connecting the bulb between the positive and ground rail (0 V) will produce the electronic circuit layout of Fig 1.14*c*.

Fig 1.14 (a)   Simple circuit   (b)   Rotated circuit   (c)   Electronic circuit

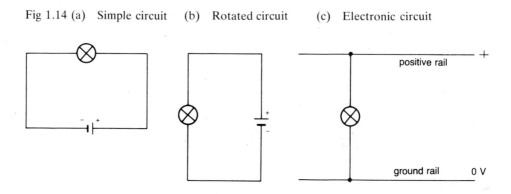

Note There must be a complete circuit in order for there to be a flow of current.

■ Resistance and Resistors

To control the flow of current in an electrical circuit, we use components that have resistance, which means they restrict the flow of current. These are called **resistors**. The symbol for a resistor is shown in Fig 1.15.

Your first assignment in the Workbook will show you how current can be controlled using resistors.

Fig 1.15   Symbol for resistor

■ Units, Symbols and Abbreviations

The electrical pressure difference (voltage) of a battery is referred to by the letter V and the unit of measurement of voltage is the **volt**. The letter V is also used as an abbreviation for volts, e.g. a battery of voltage 9 V.

The current in a circuit is referred to by a letter I and the unit of measurement of current is the ampere or **amp**. The letter A is used to abbreviate amps, e.g. a current of 0.9 amps flowing in a circuit would be written as 0.9 A.

The resistance of a component is referred to by a letter R and the unit of measurement of resistance is the **ohm**. The Greek letter omega Ω is often used as an abbreviation of ohms, e.g. a resistor with a resistance of 10 ohms would be written as 10 Ω.

The basic electrical units are usually shown as follows:

    volts   (V)   amps   (A)   ohms   (Ω).

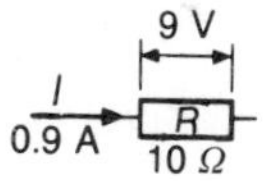

Fig 1.16   Electrical units applied to resistor

■ Resistor Colour Codes

Resistors are manufactured in a range of values. In order to recognise the value, a **colour code** is used on the resistor as shown in Fig 1.17.

The coloured bands on the resistor refer to the digits or numbers of the resistor value. The fourth colour band is usually gold or silver and it indicates the tolerance of the resistor (i.e. how accurate the resistor is with respect to its desired value). If you place the fourth tolerance band on the right, then the first coloured band on the left indicates the first digit or number of the resistor value. The value can be determined from the code. The second coloured band indicates the second digit or number of resistor value and its value can be obtained from the code. The third coloured band indicates the number of zeros in the resistor value, as indicated by the colour code.

17

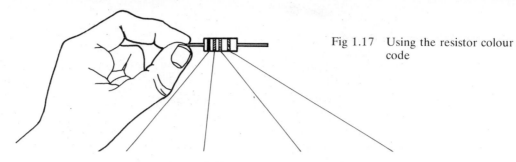

Fig 1.17   Using the resistor colour code

1st Colour Band 1st Digit		2nd Colour Band 2nd Digit		3rd Colour Band Number of Zeros		4th Colour Band Tolerance	
Black	0	Black	0	Black	No zeros	Gold	5%
Brown	1	Brown	1	Brown	One zero	Silver	10%
Red	2	Red	2	Red	Two zeros		
Orange	3	Orange	3	Orange	Three zeros		
Yellow	4	Yellow	4	Yellow	Four zeros		
Green	5	Green	5	Green	Five zeros		
Blue	6	Blue	6	Blue	Six zeros		
Violet	7	Violet	7	Violet	Seven zeros		
Grey	8	Grey	8	Grey	Eight zeros		
White	9	White	9	White	Nine zeros		

Example: green blue orange

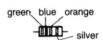 silver

1st coloured band – green – 5
2nd coloured band – blue   – 6
3rd coloured band – orange – three zeros.

Resistor is 56 000 ohms.

Large value resistors are usually expressed in kilohms (kΩ), where 1000 Ω = 1 kΩ, so the resistor is 56 kΩ.

5 *What is the resistance of resistors colour-coded as follows?*

   a)   brown   green   black   gold
   b)   red   violet   brown   gold
   c)   orange   white   red   gold
   d)   yellow   violet   yellow   gold

◼ Construction Techniques

This section is to assist you with constructing your first circuit. You need only study it if you are unfamiliar with soldering techniques. The section is only a guide – it is best for you to learn by doing the actual soldering. The basic tools you will require are shown in Fig 1.18. It is suggested that you use a 15 watt soldering iron and we will assume that the soldering iron already has a 3-pin plug attached to it. A new soldering iron bit will need to be cleaned, heated up and

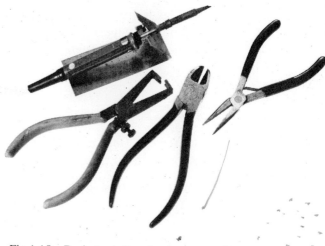

Fig 1.18   Basic tools for circuit construction

then coated with solder; this is called **tinning** the bit. If you plug in the soldering iron and switch on, it will take about two minutes for the bit to heat up to the correct temperature to melt solder. Great care should be taken as the soldering iron is hot enough to cause a nasty burn. It is also easy to burn through the PVC insulation on the soldering iron lead if you were to lay the hot bit on it. This would cause a short-circuit with the possibility of you receiving an electric shock. It is essential to rest the hot soldering iron on a metal stand, similar to the one shown in Fig 1.18, when it is not in use, as this will save the soldering iron bit burning away. The electronic components are secured to the terminal pins by soft soldering. **Soft solder** is a low temperature melting point alloy of lead and tin. If the solder is to make an effective joint between electronic components, wires and pins, a **flux** must be used. Flux is a chemical that cleans the hot metal being soldered and stops the metal oxidising with the air. The solder you will use contains a core of flux which will melt just before the solder. The leads on most electronic components are already tinned (coated with a thin layer of tin), so it is not necessary for you to tin them with solder before connecting them into a circuit.

Fig 1.19   Ground rail and positive rail
assembled on matrix board

The construction of the first circuit begins with laying out a ground rail wire and a positive (+ve) rail wire as shown in Fig 1.19. It is best to use tinned copper wire for the ground rail and positive rail. Four terminal pins are inserted in the matrix board and the tinned copper wire is wrapped round the pins and soldered in position.

The leads for connecting a battery to the circuit are then soldered in position. It is suggested that you use stranded wire for the battery leads as it is more flexible than single-strand wire (see Fig 1.20)

Fig 1.20

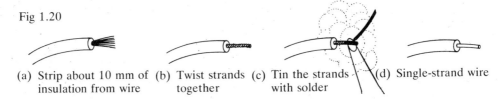

(a) Strip about 10 mm of insulation from wire (b) Twist strands together (c) Tin the strands with solder (d) Single-strand wire

The wire used to connect to the positive (+ve) terminal of the battery should have red insulation covering on it, and the battery lead for the negative terminal should have black insulation covering.

It is a good idea to use battery clips to make connection between the circuit battery leads and a 9 V battery. With the battery clips soldered to the correct leads, there is less chance of connecting to the wrong polarity terminal of the battery. Strip about 10 mm of PVC insulation from the stranded wire battery lead, twist the strands of wire and then wrap the stripped end round the terminal pin. Solder the battery leads to the terminal pins as shown in Fig 1.21. If you try out the battery clips by connecting them to a 9 V battery as shown in Fig 1.22, remember to disconnect the battery before doing any further soldering.

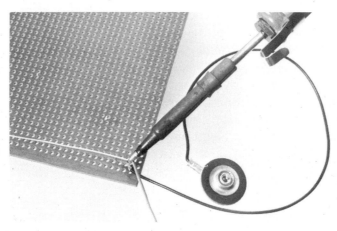

Fig 1.21   Soldering battery lead to terminal pin on ground rail

Fig 1.22   Battery clips are used to connect flying leads to the 9 V battery

Fig 1.23   Batten lamp holder soldered in
circuit

Fig 1.25   Variable resistor soldered in circuit

Fig 1.24   Try various values of resistor

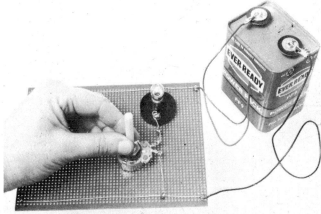

Fig 1.26   Controlling lamp brightness with a
variable resistor

*Never solder components into a circuit with battery connected. Stray currents
may damage the electronic components.*

Answers to Questions
1 The flow of water will double.
2 Pressure difference.
3 It will be greater.
4 The larger the diameter, the larger the flow.
5 a) 15 Ω   *b)* 270 Ω   *c)* 3900 Ω or 3.9 kΩ   *d)* 470 000 Ω or 470 kΩ.

21

2 The Transistor as a Switch

■ The Design Problem: A Rain Alarm

In Section 1 we looked at solutions to the problem of controlling the brightness of a lightbulb. One solution used resistors to restrict the current flowing in the circuit. Another solution was to control the current flow in the circuit with a variable resistor. Now we are going to consider a switching problem, how to turn the lightbulb 'on' and 'off' automatically. A **switch** could be used to turn the lightbulb 'on' and 'off'.

Fig 2.1 shows a circuit where the lightbulb can be turned 'on' and 'off' by operating a switch. An electric current can only flow if the switch is closed and a complete conducting path is provided.

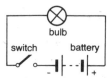

Fig 2.1   Switch used in simple circuit

In this section we are going to design a simple **electronic system** that can be used as a rain alarm. When the lightbulb is 'on' it will be used as a warning signal to indicate that it is raining. The rain alarm system will require a method of detecting the raindrops and a device to switch on the warning light. This automatic switching device is called a 'transistor'. So the design problem is to design an alarm system that gives a visible warning when it starts to rain. The problem could be stated in a block diagram form as shown in Fig 2.2.

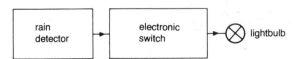

Fig 2.2   The design problem: an alarm system

Rain water is a fairly good conductor of electricity, and rain water falling on the gap between two conducting strips of metal will reduce the resistance between the strips from a very high value to about 10 kΩ. Thus a very simple **rain sensor** can be constructed from Veroboard as shown in Fig 2.3.

Fig 2.3   Simple rain sensor

The rain sensor can be used in the rain alarm system to operate a transistor which will turn the lightbulb 'on' and 'off'. We are going to use a transistor in the rain alarm system as a switch, but sometimes transistors are used as amplifiers in circuits.

1 Can you think of an everyday device that uses transistors?

■ The Transistor

In this course we shall be using **silicon transistors**. Two examples of common transistors are illustrated in Fig 2.4. The three leads of a transistor are called the **collector**, **base** and **emitter**. The leads are connected inside the metal body of the transistor to a small piece of silicon made, rather like a sandwich, from a single crystal with diffused layers of *p*-type silicon and *n*-type silicon.

Fig 2.4   Transistors

Transistors must be connected the correct way round in a circuit or they will be damaged. In order to establish which lead of the transistor is the collector or the base or the emitter, an underside view of the transistor is used (see Fig 2.5*b*). The circuit diagram symbol for the transistor is used together with the underside view to determine the leads.

Fig 2.5 (a)   The transistor

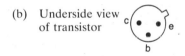

collector   emitter
base

(b)   Underside view of transistor

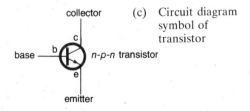

Fig 2.5*c* shows a circuit diagram symbol of the transistor. Not all transistors have this underside view as the positioning of the emitter, collector and base leads vary from one transistor to another. (An electronic engineer would look up

collector   (c)   Circuit diagram symbol of transistor

base   *n-p-n* transistor

emitter

this information in a manufacturer's book of transistor data.) This is the circuit diagram symbol for the *n-p-n*-type of transistor. Current enters the transistor along the collector lead and leaves the transistor along the emitter lead. Current flowing through the transistor is controlled by connections to the base lead.

■ The Transistor as a Switch

The transistor can be made to operate like a switch. The current in a transistor circuit, like the one shown in Fig 2.6, flows through the collector lead of the transistor and out of the emitter. Remember that conventional current flows from the

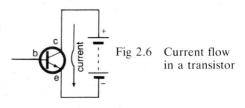

Fig 2.6   Current flow in a transistor

positive (+ve) terminal of the battery round the circuit and returns to the negative (−ve) terminal. Notice that the current flows through the transistor in the direction of the arrow on the emitter lead of the circuit diagram symbol.

When the transistor operates like a switch, it turns the current flow 'on' and 'off'. We can see this happen if a lightbulb is put in the collector part of the circuit to indicate whether current is flowing. This is shown in Fig 2.7.

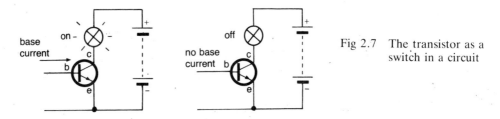

Fig 2.7   The transistor as a switch in a circuit

The transistor can be made to operate as a switch by controlling the current flowing into the base lead of the transistor. The voltage between the ground rail (−ve terminal of the battery) and the base of the transistor, determines whether current can flow through the collector to the emitter.

The current flowing into the base lead of the transistor is controlled by the voltage between the base lead and the ground rail. When no current, or a very small current, flows in the base lead the transistor is 'off', and very little current (almost nil current) flows through the collector to the emitter circuit. If a larger voltage (over about 0.6 volts) is applied between the base and the ground rail, then a current flows into the base of the transistor and it turns 'on' like a switch. When the transistor is conducting, current can flow in the collector/emitter part of the circuit. These results are summarised in Fig 2.8a and b.

Fig 2.8 (a)   (b)

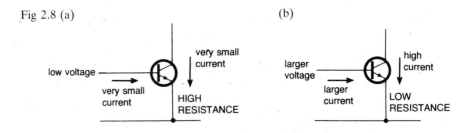

■ Biasing the Transistor

There are two main methods of switching on the transistor, and these are considered in Activity 2, Assignment 1. The methods are shown in Fig 2.9a and b and require resistors to be connected to the base of the transistor. Their selection is an important part of electronic circuit design. We call this **biasing** the transistor correctly.

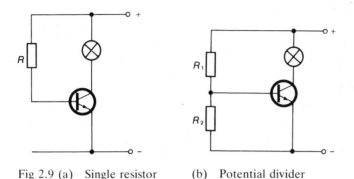

Fig 2.9 (a) Single resistor   (b) Potential divider

The resistors are used to control the current that flows in the circuit. The arrangement of resistors R_1 and R_2 in Fig 2.9b is called a **potential divider** and its function is to split up the 9 V supply voltage into appropriate proportions. For the transistor you have been using, the voltage required to switch it on is approximately 0.6 V between emitter and base. (An example of the calculation of suitable resistors for a potential divider is given later.)

■ The Rain Alarm: Development of a Solution

The problem we began considering is the design of a simple electronic rain alarm system. The alarm system requires a rain detection device (we chose a piece of Veroboard), an electronic switch (we are going to use a transistor) and a display warning device (we are going to use a lightbulb).

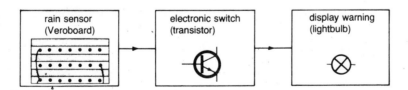

Fig. 2.10   Rain alarm system

If the lightbulb is connected in the collector circuit of a transistor, it can be made to switch 'on' and 'off' by operating the transistor as a switch. One method of biasing the transistor is to use a potential divider as shown in Fig 2.11. If resistor R_1 in the potential divider is replaced by the rain sensor

25

Veroboard, then the transistor can be switched on and off by rain water on the sensor.

When the rain sensor is dry, no current flows into the base of the transistor and the lightbulb is 'off'. If a drop of rain wets the sensor and bridges the space between the tracks, as shown in Fig 2.12b, a base current flows into the transistor which allows a collector current to flow and the lightbulb turns 'on'.

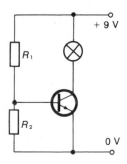

Fig 2.11   Potential divider used to bias transistor

Fig 2.12 (a)   Rain alarm in 'off' state   (b)   Rain alarm in 'on' state

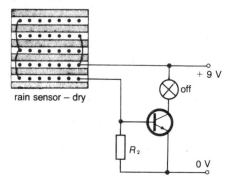
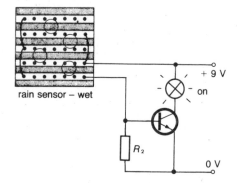

The base current can be limited by an extra 2.2 kΩ resistor in the circuit. With the circuit as it stands, it is possible for a very high base current to flow if the whole surface of the sensor became wet. Such a high current would destroy the transistor. To protect the transistor, a 2.2 kΩ resistor is placed in the base circuit as shown in Fig 2.13. If resistor R_2 is replaced by a variable resistor, the transistor circuit can be adjusted to the appropriate switching level. We now have a complete rain alarm circuit which is shown in Fig 2.14.

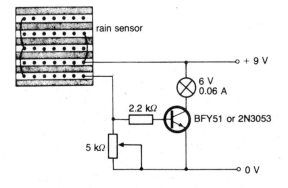

Fig 2.13   Rain alarm system

26

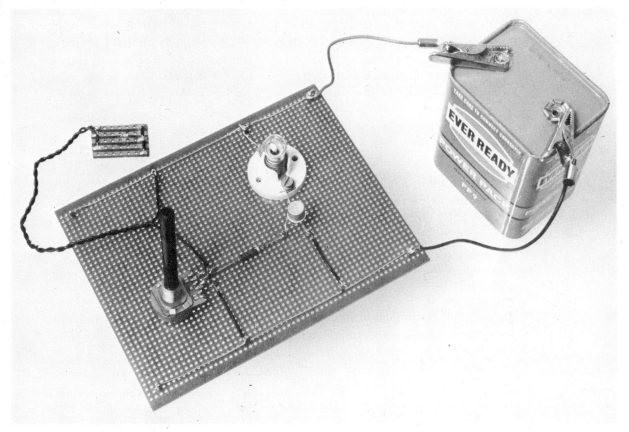

Fig. 2.14   Complete rain alarm circuit

■ Resistance

A water flow analogy for electric current was described in Section 1. The water analogy can be used to explain 'resistance'. Resistance in an electrical circuit restricts the flow of electric current. The larger the value of the resistor, the more the current is restricted and the smaller the current flowing in the circuit.

Fig 2.15 (a)   The water flow analogy   (b)   Electrical resistance

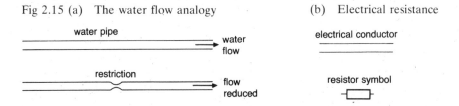

An electric current flowing in a conductor can be compared with water flowing in a pipe. If there is a restriction in the pipe, caused perhaps by squeezing a flexible pipe, this would reduce the flow of water. In a similar

27

way, if a resistor is placed in an electrical circuit, the current is reduced. The larger the value of the resistor in an electrical circuit, the smaller the current that can flow, when the applied voltage remains the same. Fig 2.16 shows a circuit where a large current flows when the resistor is a small value. When the value of the resistor is increased, the current flowing is decreased.

Fig 2.16 (a) Large current flow with small resistor   (b) Small current with large resistor

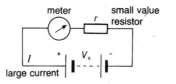 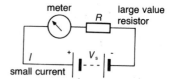

■ Resistors in Series and Parallel

Resistors can be connected in series or in parallel as shown in Fig 2.17a and b. When connected like this, a new total resistance value is created. By this means, a desired resistance value can sometimes be created from a small range of resistors of other values.

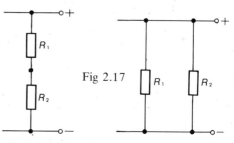

Fig 2.17

(a) Resistors in series (b) Resistors in parallel

When resistors are joined in **series** (one after the other), their combined resistance is greater than their individual resistances. The combined series resistance R_s is given by $R_s = R_1 + R_2$.

$$R_s = R_1 + R_2$$

Fig 2.18   Resistors in series

When resistors are joined in **parallel** (side by side), their combined resistance is less than their individual resistances. The combined parallel resistance R_p is given by $\dfrac{1}{R_p} = \dfrac{1}{R_1} + \dfrac{1}{R_2}$, also $R_p = \dfrac{R_1 \times R_2}{R_1 + R_2}$.

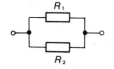

Fig 2.19   Resistors in parallel

Example 1

Two resistors, each 100 Ω, are joined in series. What is the resistance between A and B?
Combined series resistance $R_s = R_1 + R_2$

$$= 100\ \Omega + 100\ \Omega$$
$$= 200\ \Omega.$$

So the combined resistance is 200 Ω.

28

Example 2
Two resistors, R_1 and R_2, are joined in series.
$R_1 = 8000\ \Omega$ and $R_2 = 1000\ \Omega$.
What is the resistance between A and B?
Combined series resistance $R_s = R_1 + R_2$

$$= 8000\ \Omega + 1000\ \Omega$$
$$= 9000\ \Omega$$
$$= 9\ k\Omega.$$

So the combined series resistance is 9 kΩ.

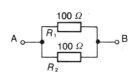

Example 3
Two resistors, each 100 Ω, are joined in parallel.
What is the resistance between A and B?

Combined parallel resistance R_p is given by $\dfrac{1}{R_p} = \dfrac{1}{R_1} + \dfrac{1}{R_2} = \dfrac{1}{100} + \dfrac{1}{100}$

$$\frac{1}{R_p} = \frac{2}{100}$$

$$R_p = \frac{100}{2} = 50\ \Omega.$$

So the combined parallel resistance R_p is 50 Ω.

Example 4
Two resistors, R_1 and R_2, are joined in parallel.
$R_1 = 400\ \Omega$ and $R_2 = 100\ \Omega$.
What is the resistance between A and B?

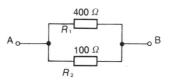

Combined parallel resistance R_p is given by $\dfrac{1}{R_p} = \dfrac{1}{R_1} + \dfrac{1}{R_2}$

$$\frac{1}{R_p} = \frac{1}{400} + \frac{1}{100} = \frac{1 + 4}{400}$$

$$\frac{1}{R_p} = \frac{5}{400}$$

$$R_p = \frac{400}{5} = 80\ \Omega.$$

So the combined parallel resistance R_p is 80 Ω.

2 *What would be the combined series resistance of the two resistors*
$R_1 = 400\ \Omega$ and $R_2 = 100\ \Omega$?

■ Preferred Values of Resistance

Resistors are not manufactured for all values. Only certain values are available and these are called **preferred values**. These values are: 1, 1.2, 1.5, 1.8, 2.2, 2.7, 3.3, 3.9, 4.7, 5.6, 6.8; 8.2 and the 10, 100, 1000, 10 000, 100 000 and 1 000 000 times multipliers of these. So for some of the previous examples, we would need to choose the nearest values available.

■ Ohm's Law

In previous sections we have seen that both voltage and resistance affect the current in a circuit. Ohm's Law states that, for a conductor at a constant temperature, the current flowing through the conductor is directly proportional to the potential difference between its ends. This can be expressed mathematically as:

voltage = current × resistance or $V = I \times R$.

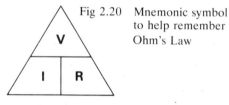

A convenient way of remembering this equation is shown in Fig 2.20 as a mnemonic symbol. To use this figure, cover the quantity you want to find and the method of calculating it is left visible. Use Fig 2.20 to find equations for I and R.

Fig 2.20 Mnemonic symbol to help remember Ohm's Law

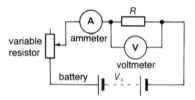

Ohm's Law can be demonstrated by connecting up the circuit shown in Fig 2.21. The potential difference across resistor R is shown by the voltmeter V and is altered by adjusting the variable resistor. The ammeter A shows the current flowing through R. V and A are both read for different settings of the variable resistor and a graph is plotted of potential difference against current, similar to that shown in Fig 2.22.

Fig 2.21 Circuit to demonstrate Ohm's Law

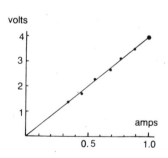

The slope of the graph of voltage against current represents the resistance of the conductor, i.e. slope of graph

Fig 2.22 Graph of voltage against current for a resistor

$$= \frac{V}{I} = \frac{4 \text{ volts}}{1 \text{ amp}} = 4\,\Omega.$$

So the resistance of the conductor is 4 Ω.

☐ Use of Ohm's Law to Calculate Resistance Values

It is sometimes necessary to design a potential divider which may be used to provide a bias for a transistor.

If a potential divider is to be used to bias the transistor (as in Fig 2.23) and the transistor is to remain turned full 'on', then a voltage of well over 0.6 volts is required across the base/emitter junction. If 2 volts are required to turn the transistor full 'on', this base/emitter voltage can be supplied by a potential divider as shown in Fig 2.24.

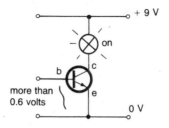

Fig 2.23 'Turn on' voltage

Fig 2.24 Using the potential divider to bias the transistor

If we assume the current through the potential divider is to be 1 mA (0.001 A), then we can calculate the total resistance of the potential divider. Potential dividers are usually designed so that the current flow through the resistor is about ten times the current flowing into the base of the transistor. This will be explained in more detail later.

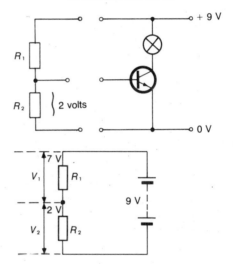

Using Ohm's Law, we can calculate the total resistance of $R_1 + R_2$, where a current of 1 mA flows as a result of applying a voltage of 9 volts (see Fig 2.25).

Fig 2.25 Potential divider

$$R = \frac{V}{I} = \frac{9}{0.001}$$

$$= 9000 \ \Omega$$

$$\therefore R = 9 \ k\Omega.$$

If the 2 volts is to be produced across resistor R_2 and a current of 1 mA is flowing through R_2 then

$$R_2 = \frac{V}{I} = \frac{2}{0.001}$$

$$= 2000 \ \Omega$$

$$\therefore R_2 = 2 \ k\Omega.$$

Since R_1 and R_2 are in series,
$$R_1 + R_2 = 9000 \ \Omega$$
$$R_1 + 2000 = 9000$$
$$R_1 = 9000 - 2000 = 7000 \ \Omega$$
$$\therefore R_1 = 7 \ k\Omega$$

The voltage drop across R_1 will be 7 volts since
$$V_1 = IR$$
$$V_1 = 0.001 \times 7000$$
$$V_1 = 7 \ \text{volts.}$$

Notice the ratio of $\dfrac{R_1}{R_2}$ is the same as $\dfrac{V_1}{V_2}$.

Actually, you cannot buy 7 kΩ or 2 kΩ resistors. The nearest preferred values would be 6.8 kΩ and 2.2 kΩ.

☐ Tolerance

The value of a particular resistor can vary slightly either side of the stated value. This is called the **tolerance** and is represented by the fourth band of the resistor colour coding.

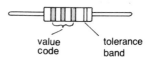

Fig 2.26   Tolerance band on a resistor

Tolerances: gold 5%, silver 10%.

Example
What is the possible range of values of a resistor which is colour-coded brown, black, brown, silver?

This resistor is 100 Ω ± 10%
10% of 100 Ω is 10 Ω.
So the resistor value could lie between 90 Ω and 110 Ω.

Answers to Questions
1 Transistor radio.
2 R_s = 500 Ω.

3 Light-sensitive Circuits

■ The Transistor

In the last section we used an *n-p-n*
transistor (*p*-type material with
n-type either side). Later in the
course we shall use *p-n-p* transistors
(*n*-type silicon with *p*-type either
side). Externally they often look the
same but they need to be connected
differently – so be careful.

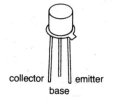

Fig 3.1   The transistor

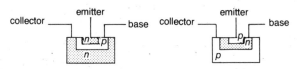

Fig 3.2   Transistor construction

The circuit diagram symbols for the two kinds of transistor can be distinguished by the arrowhead on the emitter lead (see Fig 3.3).

Fig 3.3   Circuit diagram symbols

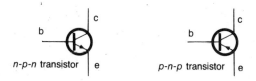

The direction of the arrowhead on the emitter is a useful way of remembering the direction of **conventional current** flow in a circuit diagram. For both
the *n-p-n* transistor and the *p-n-p* transistor the arrowhead on the emitter
shows the direction of the base/emitter current and also the collector/emitter
current in the circuit.

Fig 3.4   Conventional current flow through a transistor

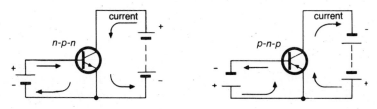

☐ Biasing the Transistor

It is very important to connect the terminals of a battery the correct way round in a transistor circuit. An *n-p-n* transistor must have the battery terminals connected with the positive (+ve) terminal towards the collector lead. For the transistor to act like a switch and conduct, allowing current to flow from the collector into the emitter part of the circuit, a positive voltage must be applied across the base/emitter of the transistor.

The voltage at the base must be more positive than the emitter. This is called **biasing** the transistor. If the positive bias voltage must be more than 0.6 volts, a cell giving 1.5 volts would be a suitable way of biasing the transistor. When the positive terminal of the cell is connected to the base, a current flows in the base/emitter part of the circuit, the transistor turns 'on' and a larger current flows from the collector into the emitter of the circuit.

A *p-n-p* transistor must be connected with the negative terminals of the battery towards the collector lead of the transistor. A negative bias voltage of more than 0.6 volts must be applied to the base of the silicon *p-n-p* transistor to make it switch 'on'. If a 1.5 volt cell was used to provide the negative bias, the negative terminal must be connected to the base of the transistor.

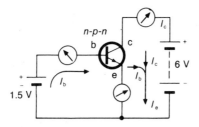

Fig 3.5   Biasing an *n-p-n* transistor

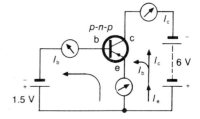

Fig 3.6   Biasing a *p-n-p* transistor

■ The Transistor Switch

The transistor switch developed in the previous section is shown in Fig 3.7. To make the bulb light up, the transistor must be made to conduct a current through the collector/emitter part of the circuit. To operate the transistor switch, a positive voltage of more than 0.6 volts must be applied between the base and the emitter leads.

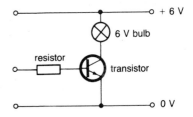

Fig 3.7   Transistor switch

   1 What is the minimum positive voltage that must be applied across the base/emitter junction of a silicon transistor to turn the transistor 'on'?

The 'turn on' voltage can be demonstrated with the circuit shown in Fig 3.8. A voltmeter is placed across the base/emitter junction of the transistor to record the 'turn on' voltage, which is about 0.6 volts for a silicon transistor and about 0.2 volts for a germanium transistor. The bias voltage is varied with a variable resistor of value 50 kΩ. Using a 0 to 1 volt scale voltmeter the 'turn on' voltage is measurable.

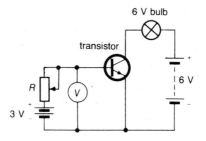

Fig 3.8 'Turn on' voltage of a transistor

There are three different methods of providing a positive voltage to the base of the transistor so that more than 0.6 volts is available to 'turn on' the transistor switch. This can be done with a cell or low voltage battery, a single resistor, or a pair of resistors called a **potential divider**. The next few sections will be concentrated on using the potential divider to bias a transistor.

Fig 3.9   Methods of biasing a transistor

   (a) Single cell   (b) Single resistor   (c) Potential divider – two resistors

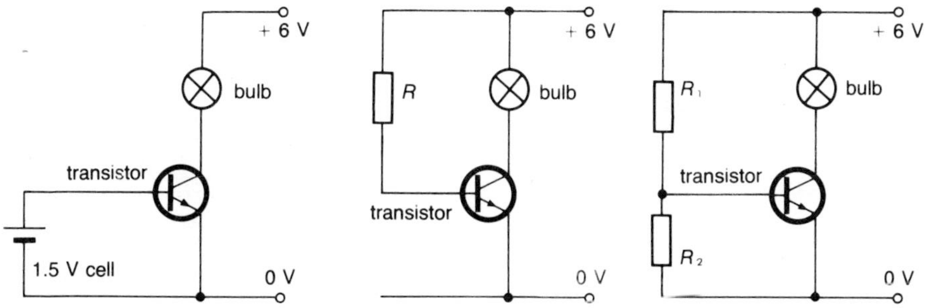

The Potential Divider

(*Revision* – read only if you do not understand the term 'potential divider'.)

If two resistors, one of 200 ohms and one of 700 ohms, are connected in series and then connected to the terminals of a 9 volt battery, a total of 9 volts is dropped across the resistors. The total resistance of the two resistors is 200 + 700 ohms = 900 ohms. The same current runs through both resistors so, by Ohm's Law, voltage = current × resistance.

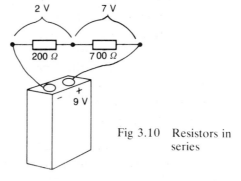

Fig 3.10   Resistors in series

The voltage drop across each resistor is proportional to their resistance.

Voltage drop across the 200 ohm resistor $= 9 \text{ V} \times \dfrac{200}{900}$

$= 2 \text{ volts.}$

Voltage drop across the 700 ohm resistor $= 9 \text{ V} \times \dfrac{700}{900}$

$= 7 \text{ volts.}$

A potential divider is shown in Fig 3.11. The two resistors connected in series are placed between the positive 9 volt rail and the 0 volt rail. A total of 9 volts is still connected across the series resistance of (200 + 700) ohms, 900 ohms. Since 2 volts is dropped across the 200 ohm resistor, the point between the resistors in the potential divider is 2 volts higher than the 0 volt rail. Therefore this point between the resistors is + 2 volts.

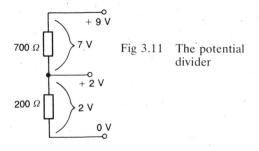

Fig 3.11   The potential divider

The potential divider is a useful method of providing the positive bias voltage for an *n-p-n* transistor.

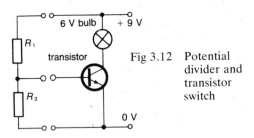

Fig 3.12   Potential divider and transistor switch

2 *If the resistors R_1 = 700 ohms and R_2 = 200 ohms were used in the potential divider shown in Fig 3.11 and the potential divider and the transistor switch were connected together, would the lightbulb be 'on' or 'off'?*

■ **Design Problem**

The problem is to design an electronic system where a lightbulb can be controlled by the intensity of light falling on the system.

This problem could have been stated in a graphical form by saying that we required an electronic circuit to control a lightbulb, and a component in the circuit must respond to the amount of light falling on it.

Fig 3.13   The design problem

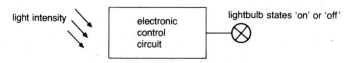

If a light-sensitive device, called a **light-dependent resistor (LDR)**, is used in the potential divider and is connected to the transistor switch, it will provide a simple solution to the problem.

Fig 3.14   Block diagram of simple design solution

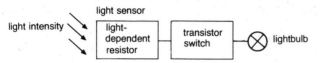

■ The Light-dependent Resistor (LDR)

A light-dependent resistor is made from **cadmium sulphide** which is a semiconductor material whose resistance changes according to the amount of light falling on it. The resistance of the LDR is about 10 megohms (10 MΩ) in total darkness and falls to about 150 ohms in bright light. Try to remember:

dark – high resistance;
bright light – low resistance.

Fig 3.15   Typical light-dependent resistor

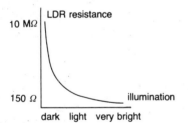

Fig 3.16   Graph of resistance of LDR against illumination

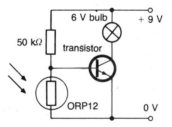

Fig 3.17   A light-dependent transistor switch

The ORP12 is one typical kind of light-dependent resistor with a cadmium sulphide cell mounted in a clear resin block with two soldering leads. Like most resistors, it does not matter which way round an LDR is mounted in a circuit.

If we replace one resistor of the potential divider with an LDR, it is like having a variable resistor in the circuit which alters its value when the light intensity changes. When the LDR is covered and placed in total darkness, its resistance increases, the votage across the base/emitter rises, the transistor begins to conduct and the lightbulb turns 'on'.

37

■ Light-sensitive Circuits

In a practical circuit it is necessary to adjust the light-dependent transistor switch for different levels of light intensity, and so the other resistor of the potential divider is replaced with a variable resistor (potentiometer).

When a variable resistor is put in the potential divider part of the circuit, it is possible to adjust its value down to zero resistance and place a high voltage across the base/emitter of the transistor. To protect the transistor from too large currents in the base, a fixed resistor is inserted between the LDR/ variable resistor and the transistor.

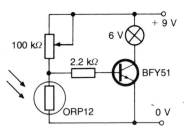

Fig 3.18   Bulb lights when LDR is in the dark

Fig 3.19   Bulb lights when LDR is in a light beam

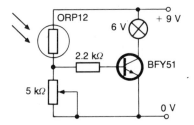

The action of the light-dependent switch can be reversed by changing the positions of the LDR and the variable resistor in the circuit. A different value variable resistor is now required. The lightbulb will turn 'off' when the LDR is covered and turn 'on' when a light beam is shone on the LDR. A more sensitive photoswitch is made by adding a second transistor to act as an amplifier in the circuit. This will be discussed in more detail in the next section.

Answers to Questions
1 About 0.6 volts.
2 'On'.

38

4 Interface Devices

■ The Photoswitch Circuit and Electromagnetic Devices

A photoswitch circuit was described in the previous section. A light-dependent resistor (LDR) and a resistor were used as a potential divider to bias a transistor. If the resistor was replaced by a variable resistor, the circuit could be operated in different lighting levels.

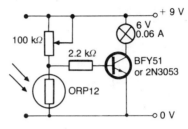

Fig 4.1   Photoswitch circuit

In this circuit, the transistor functioned as a switch. The lightbulb could automatically be turned on by covering the LDR. When the light-dependent resistor was in the dark, the voltage across it was greater than 0.6 volts, which is the voltage required across the base/emitter junction of the transistor to make it conduct.

The addition of an extra transistor makes the circuit switching action more sensitive. The second transistor acts as an amplifier. This circuit is shown in Fig 4.2. When the LDR is covered, the lightbulb 'turns on'. The voltage required to operate the lightbulb is 6 V. The **output voltage** between the positive rail and the collector lead of the transistor is about 8 volts. A small voltage drop occurs across the collector/emitter of the transistor. Fig 4.3 shows the output voltage, which could be used to operate several different low voltage electrical devices, such as motors, solenoids, bells or counters.

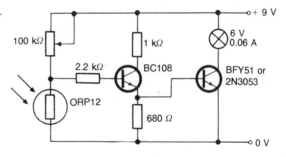

Fig 4.2   More sensitive photoswitch circuit

Fig 4.3   Output voltage from photoswitch circuit

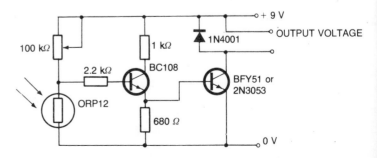

39

The transistor BFY51 or 2N3053 is capable of carrying a current up to 1 amp through the collector/emitter circuit. So electrical devices like solenoids, motors, bells and counters that require operating currents up to 1 amp can be switched on by the photoswitch circuit.

An **electric motor** is a machine for converting electrical energy into mechanical energy. We can use electric motors to provide rotary motion in projects which require a mechanical energy input.

Small electric motors, which could be used to operate models or small projects, can work on low voltages of 6 or 9 volts. A low voltage dc electric motor is shown in Fig 4.4.

Fig 4.4   Small dc electric motor

The dc motor has permanent magnets which provide the stationary magnetic field (see Fig 4.5). The rotating armature of the motor is mounted in the magnetic field. The armature consists of several wire coils wound round an iron core and connected to a commutator. When an electric current is passed through the armature coil, it rotates. Current is picked up through the commutator from brushes. Fig 4.6 shows a section through a small permanent magnet electric motor.

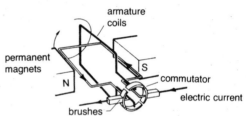

Fig 4.5   The dc motor principle

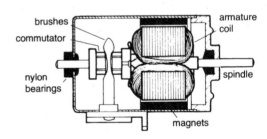

Fig 4.6   Section through a small permanent magnet motor

The circuit diagram symbol for an electric motor is shown in Fig 4.7.

Fig 4.7   Circuit diagram symbol for electric motor

A solenoid is a device for converting electrical energy into mechanical energy, which appears in the form of linear motion. A current-carrying coil of wire is called a **solenoid**. The current flowing through the coil produces a magnetic field around the coil as shown in Fig 4.8. The strength of the magnetic field can be increased and concentrated by inserting a soft iron core into the

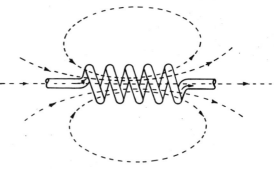

Fig 4.8 · Magnetic field of solenoid

coil. When a current passes through the coil, the soft iron core becomes magnetic. This device is called an **electromagnet** (see Fig 4.9). Solenoid coils are usually wound on a non-metallic former. When an electric current is passed through a hollow solenoid, the magnetic field produced pulls an iron core into the centre of the coil. The attraction of the iron core into the solenoid produces linear motion (see Fig 4.10). This mechanical action can be used to operate valves and switches. It might be used in projects to act as a remote door bolt or an automatic catch.

Fig 4.9   Electromagnet   Fig 4.10   Solenoid

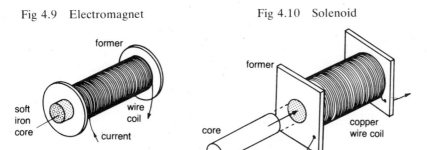

The strength of the solenoid magnetic field is dependent on the current flowing through the coil, and also on the number of turns of wire on the coil. The circuit diagram symbol for the solenoid is shown in Fig 4.11a and the symbol for an electromagnet in Fig 4.11b. Low voltage (6 volts) solenoids can be obtained and could be operated by the photoswitch circuit.

Fig 4.11   Circuit diagram symbol for (a) solenoid   (b) electromagnet

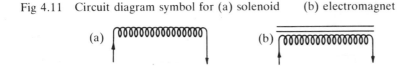

Low voltage electric bells are also obtainable and could be used with the photoswitch. An **electric bell** makes use of two electromagnets (see Fig 4.12).

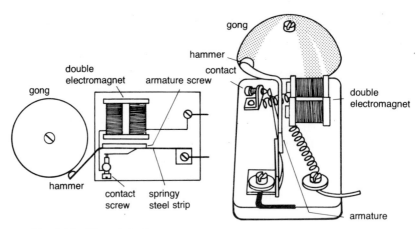

Fig 4.12   Electric bell

A hammer is attached to an armature which is attracted towards the double electromagnet. A make-and-break contact opens the circuit when the armature is attracted to the double electromagnet. As soon as the circuit is broken, the armature is released from the electromagnets, and hence a to-and-fro movement of the hammer on a gong is produced.

The electric bell circuit diagram symbol is shown in Fig 4.13.

Fig 4.13   Circuit diagram symbol for electric bell

The principle of operation of an electromagnet is used in the **electromagnetic counter**. When a current is passed through the coil, a pivoted lever is attracted towards the core of the electromagnet (see Fig 4.14). Each time the lever moves, it advances a geared number wheel. The numbered wheel moves through one tenth of a revolution each time a pulse of current passes through the coil. In the counter shown in Fig 4.14, four numbers display the thousands, hundreds, tens and units. This is a four-digit counter. Low voltage (6 volts) counters are available and they have low value resistance coils.

Fig 4.14   Electromagnetic counter

We shall use the graphic symbol shown in Fig 4.15 to represent an electromagnetic counter.

Fig 4.15   Circuit diagram symbol for electromagnetic counter

Any of these low voltage electromagnetic devices could be used at the output of the photoswitch circuit. The light-dependent resistor and transistor circuit could operate a small motor, a solenoid, an electric bell or a counter, as shown in Fig 4.16.

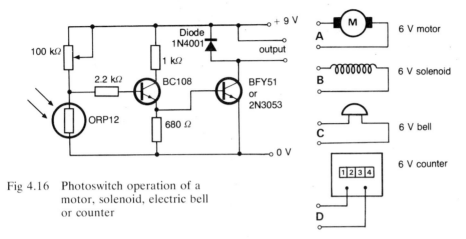

Fig 4.16 Photoswitch operation of a motor, solenoid, electric bell or counter

Each of the electromagnetic devices described is capable of producing a small voltage, called a back voltage, when the device is switched off. This back voltage could damage the transistors in the circuit, so a diode is placed across the output to protect the transistors. (This is explained in more detail in later lessons.)

The photoswitch circuit in Fig 4.16 operates from one power source, a 9 volt battery. The circuit operating from this battery will be called the **primary circuit**.

■ Design Problem: A Counting System

Suppose we wanted to design a system to count people as they walked through a doorway. The number of people passing through the doorway is to be displayed on a six digit 24 V electromagnetic counter (see Fig 4.17).

One possible solution might be to have a light beam shining on an LDR. When a person interrupts the light beam, a transistor switch would activate the counter. The system is shown in Fig 4.18.

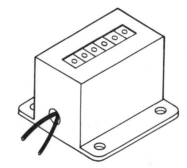

Fig 4.17 24 V electromagnetic counter

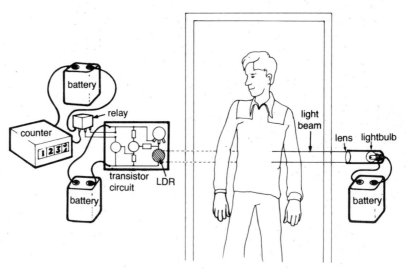

Fig 4.18   Electronic system for counting people

This simple counting system could be represented in a block diagram as shown in Fig 4.19.

Fig 4.19   Block diagram of electronic system to count people

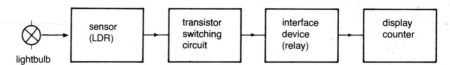

The transistor photoswitch circuit requires a 9 V power supply. We have called this the primary circuit. It will produce an output voltage of about 8 V when the LDR is covered. The counter operates on 24 V and it will require its own 24 V power supply and circuit. Let us call this circuit the **secondary circuit**. A device is required to connect between the primary and secondary circuits. A suitable interface device might be a relay (see Fig 4.20).

A **relay** is an electromagnetic

Fig 4.20   Relay

device that changes switching contacts when it receives an electric signal. The relay is really an application of an electromagnet. It consists of a wire coil with a soft iron core, as shown in Fig 4.21.

When a small control current is passed through the coil, the soft iron core is magnetised. A pivoted armature is attracted towards the magnetised core. The movement of this armature closes contacts 1 and 2 (in Fig 4.21) and opens contacts 2 and 3. It could be said that the movement had changed over the contacts 1 and 3. The contacts can be used to control larger currents in a secondary circuit. The relay is really a type of switch. Its main function is to control large currents in secondary circuits by a small current passing through the coil.

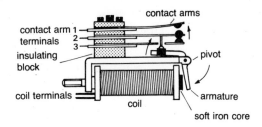

Fig 4.21   Relay

Fig 4.22   Circuit diagram symbol for relay

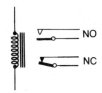

One method of representing the relay in a circuit diagram, is to use the symbol shown in Fig 4.22. The symbol consists of a coil and two sets of contacts, one normally open (NO), and the other normally closed (NC). When a current is passed through the coil, the NO contacts close, and the NC contacts open.

An alternative method of representing a relay is to use the circuit diagram symbol shown in Fig 4.23. The resistance of the relay coil is indicated in the relay symbol box, in this example it is 185 ohms. If there are several relays in a circuit, they might be labelled RLA, RLB and RLC. The number of contacts used on the relay is indicated under the label.

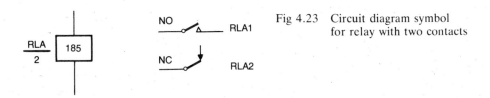

Fig 4.23   Circuit diagram symbol for relay with two contacts

Thus $\dfrac{RLA}{2}$ is relay A with 2 contacts.

Note this relay has one contact RLA1, which is normally open (NO), and a second contact RLA2, which is normally closed (NC).

The people-counting system requires a primary circuit for the LDR and switching transistors with a 9 V power supply and a secondary circuit, with a 24 V power supply, to operate the counter. The circuits are coupled with a relay but only one set of contacts is used; this is the normally open set of contacts. The complete system is shown in Fig 4.24.

Fig 4.24 Electronic system for counting objects

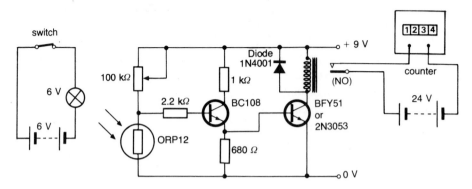

Since the relay is an electromagnetic device, it can generate a back voltage, so a diode must be included in the circuit to protect the transistors.

■ Design Problem: A Photoswitch Burglar Alarm

Suppose we wanted to design a burglar alarm system to protect items of jewellery in a display cabinet. We intend to use a light beam and an LDR to sense the intruder. A transistor circuit can be switched by interruption of the light beam and a relay might be used to operate an electric bell. The situation is shown in Fig 4.25. The electric bell operates from a 12 V power supply.

Fig 4.25 Photoswitch burglar alarm

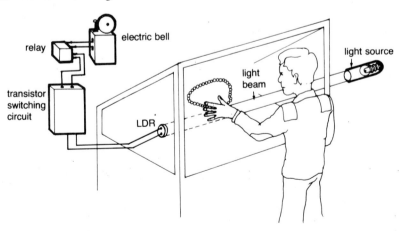

The solution to this burglar alarm problem can be expressed in the form of a block diagram as shown in Fig 4.26.

Fig 4.26   Block diagram for burglar alarm

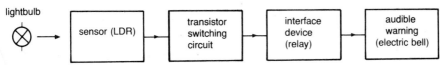

When the burglar breaks the light beam, the electric bell must ring as a warning alarm. The electric bell 12 V circuit can be coupled to the 9 V transistor photoswitch circuit with a relay. As soon as the light beam is broken by an intruder, the bell must ring continuously. It is no use if the burglar alarm stops when the light beam is completed after the intruder moves away from the cabinet. The relay must be made to hold on, and keep the bell ringing as soon as the beam is broken. This is achieved by using a second set of relay contacts. The contacts are connected across the second transistor as shown in Fig 4.27.

When the burglar interrupts the light beam, the resistance of the LDR rises and the transistors are switched on, allowing a current to pass through the relay coil. The second set of relay contacts allows a current to by-pass the second transistor and hold the relay on – even after the burglar has moved away. This effect of holding a relay on, after the initial coil current has passed,

Fig 4.27   Use of second set of contacts to 'latch up' relay

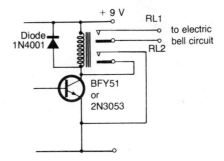

is called **latching** the relay. It is necessary to put a diode across the relay coil to protect the transistors from back voltages. The complete burglar alarm system is shown in Fig 4.28.

Fig 4.28   Circuit diagram of burglar alarm system

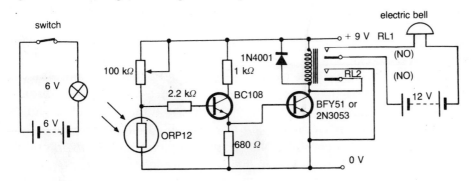

47

☐ Interface Devices

An interface device, like a relay, can be used to couple together a primary and secondary circuit. Instead of a relay to connect two circuits, we could use a dry reed switch and reed coil or a reed relay. A small current through the coil of the interface device can control large currents in the secondary circuit.

Fig 4.29 Interface device to couple circuits

A **dry reed switch** is a glass envelope with two metal contacts inside. The contacts are made of a ferrous metal (metal containing iron) which is gold or silver plated. These flat contacts are called reeds. The glass envelope is filled with an inert gas, such as nitrogen, to prevent the corrosion of the reeds. The dry reed switch will act as 'proximity' switch if a permanent magnet is brought close to it. The magnetic field of the magnet causes one reed to act as a north pole and the other reed to act as a south magnetic pole. Unlike magnetic poles are attracted and the reed switch closes (see Fig 4.30).

Fig 4.30 (a)   Dry reed switch   (b)   Closing the reed switch with a permanent magnet

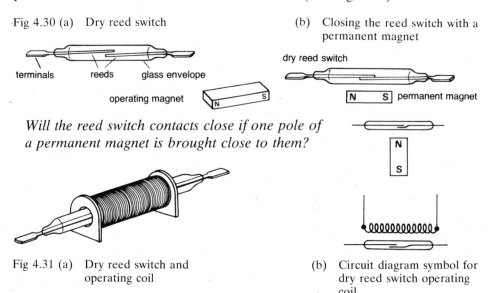

Will the reed switch contacts close if one pole of a permanent magnet is brought close to them?

Fig 4.31 (a)   Dry reed switch and operating coil   (b)   Circuit diagram symbol for dry reed switch operating coil

The dry reed switch can be closed by the magnetic field of a coil. You will recall that a coil has a magnetic field around it when a current passes through the coil. The strongest part of the magnetic field is at the centre of the coil. If the dry reed switch is placed at the centre of the coil, it will operate if a current is passed through the **operating coil**. A typical dry reed switch and operating coil is shown assembled on a base board with sockets in Fig 4.32.

Fig 4.32 Dry reed switch in operating coil (assembled on matrix board with sockets)

The dry reed switch and operating coil can be used to couple a primary transistor circuit to a secondary circuit. For example, Fig 4.33 shows a photoswitch circuit coupled to an electric motor circuit, using a dry reed switch and operating coil.

Fig 4.33 Photoswitch circuit coupled to electric motor with dry reed switch and operating coil

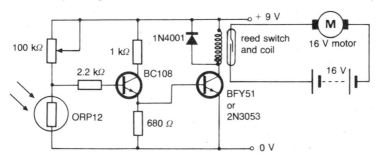

It is possible to purchase the reed switch and coil encapsulated in a plastic package. This is called a **reed relay**. The reed relay shown in Fig 4.34 could be used as an interface device to couple together a primary and secondary circuit. Reed relays can only be used for currents up to 200 mA.

Some reed relays, especially the DIL type, have a diode included in the plastic package. These dual-in-line reed relays must be connected the correct way round in a circuit (see Fig 4.34c).

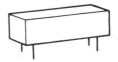

Fig 4.34 (a) Reed relay

(b) Internal connections of reed relay

(c) DIL reed relay

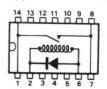

■ Circuit Applications

There are numerous projects that could make use of the photoswitch circuit previously described, and many problems where use of this circuit is a possible solution. Here, only a few situations are described where the photo-switch circuit might be used.

Animal traps

The photoswitch circuit can be used with a light beam for detection purposes. For example, if you wanted to trap a small animal without harming it, you might detect the presence of the animal with a light beam and LDR, and trigger a solenoid holding a trap door. Fig 4.35 shows a possible solution to the animal trap problem.

Fig 4.35 (a)   Animal trap

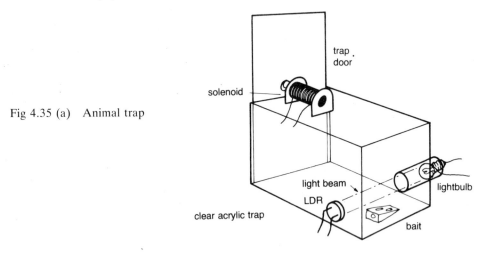

(b)   Possible circuit for animal trap

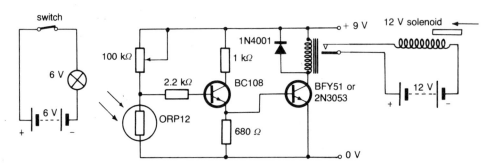

50

Light-seeking Vehicle

The photoswitch circuit would require some minor adjustments if it were used to switch a motor on when you shone a torchlight at the LDR.

Such a circuit could be attached to a small vehicle to control the drive motor. Small vehicles require a powerful motor to drive the wheels. You could use a Meccano motor or perhaps a 16 V motor like the one shown in Fig 4.36.

Fig 4.36   Low voltage electric motor for vehicle propulsion

The basic photoswitch circuit would require a different value variable resistor. The position of the LDR would need to be altered if the motor was to be controlled by a light beam (see Fig 4.37).

Fig 4.37   Light-seeking vehicle circuit diagram

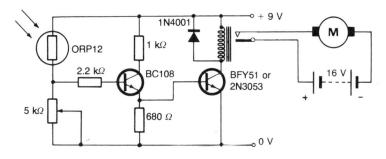

Answer to Question

No, because both reeds are now the same magnetic pole.

ADDITIONAL NOTES

Using a Relay

A relay contains an electromagnet. When the relay is turned 'off' a large back voltage, called a back **electromotive force (emf)** is produced. The changing magnetic field induces a voltage in the coil which causes a current to flow in the opposite direction to the original relay operating current, i.e. it flows backwards. The faster the magnetic field changes, the larger the voltage difference (or emf) momentarily produced across the ends of the coil. This voltage difference is the **back emf** and it can damage the transistors in a circuit.

Whenever a relay is used in a circuit, a diode is placed across the relay coil. The diode allows the back emf, which is in the opposite direction to the battery voltage, to go through it rather than damage the transistors.

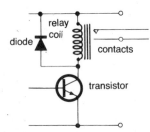

Fig 4.38   Protection of transistors by a diode across a relay coil

A **diode** is an electronic component that will allow a current to pass in one direction (the forward direction). Actually, a very small current can pass in the reverse direction. The diode action could be demonstrated by use of a 1.5 V cell and lightbulb as shown in Fig 4.39.

Fig 4.39   Demonstrating current flow through a diode

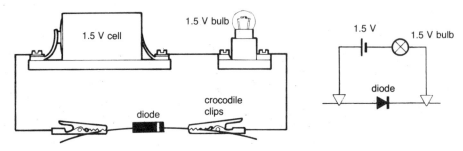

When a current passes through the diode in the forward direction (as indicated by the arrow direction of the circuit diagram symbol), the lightbulb will be 'on'. In the reverse direction, the lightbulb will be 'off' (see Fig 4.40).

Fig 4.40   The diode in a circuit
(a)   Passes current in a forward direction
(b)   No current (or very little current) in a reverse direction

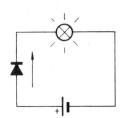
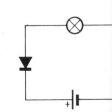

A suitable diode for use in the photoswitch circuit might be the 1N4001 silicon diode. The band round the diode indicates the bar end of the circuit diagram symbol for a diode (see Fig 4.41).

Fig 4.41 (a) Diode (b) Circuit diagram symbol for diode

Most relays have several sets of contacts which are silver, platinum or gold plated. The dc resistance of the relay coil is shown in the rectangle of the relay circuit diagram symbol (see Fig 4.42).

Fig 4.42 Relay circuit

The contacts of the relay can be shown normally closed (NC) as in Fig 4.43a, or normally open (NO) as in Fig 4.43b. Relays can also be used to change over (CO) contacts. The change-over would either break contact 1 before making contact 2 (see Fig 4.43c) or the change-over would make contact 1 before breaking contact 2 (see Fig 4.43d).

Fig 4.43 Relay contacts

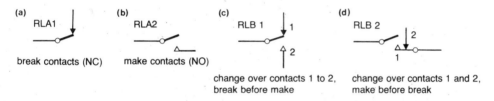

The table below is given to help you work out the contact connection numbers on continental pattern relays.

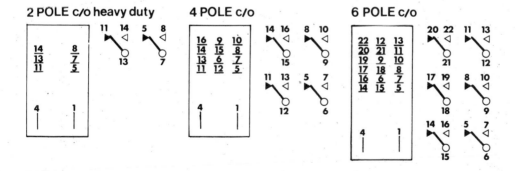

53

5 Temperature-switching Circuits

■ Measuring Current and Potential Difference

The movement of electrons through a conductor is called an electric current. We can measure the electric current with a type of meter called an **ammeter**. The rate of current flow is measured in **amperes (amps)**. Since current flows through all the components in a circuit, it is essential to put the ammeter in series with the other components in the circuit.

An ammeter is put in series in a circuit to measure the current (see Fig 5.1). Notice the ammeter must be connected with its positive terminal towards the positive terminal of the battery.

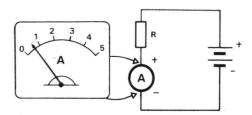

Fig 5.1   An ammeter must be connected in series in a circuit

The current is produced by a source of electrical pressure in the circuit; this might be a cell or a battery. Electrical pressure difference or **potential difference** is measured in volts.

The potential difference at points in a circuit is measured with a meter called a **voltmeter**. To measure the potential difference between two points in a circuit or the voltage across a component, the voltmeter is connected in parallel with the component. The voltmeter connection is shown in Fig 5.2.

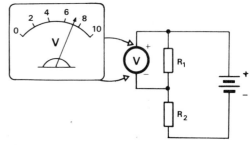

Fig 5.2   A voltmeter must be connected in parallel with a component in a circuit

☐ Meters

Moving-coil meters can be used to measure both current and potential difference. The current to be measured is passed through a coil which is suspended in a magnetic field (see Fig 5.3). The larger the current flowing through the coil, the more the coil moves. This type of meter is called a **moving-coil meter**. The coil is mounted in jewelled bearings. It is restored to its zero position by two fine spiral springs, which are also connected to the

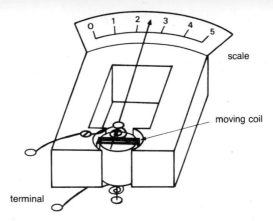

Fig 5.3   Moving coil meter

terminals. A pointer is attached to the moving coil. As the current through the coil increases, the pointer moves across the face of the scale. The movement of the pointer from zero to the end of the scale is called the **full scale deflection (fsd)** of the meter.

Meters are selected by the current that will cause a full scale deflection of the meter. For example, you could buy a moving-coil meter with an fsd of 100 μA, or an fsd of 1 mA. Meters are adapted to measure amps or volts by the use of shunt resistors and series resistors. A **shunt** or parallel resistor can be used with a small current meter to measure larger currents. An ammeter with an fsd of 1 mA might be used with a shunt resistor to measure currents up to, say, 10 mA.

Consider the circuit shown in Fig 5.4. If a 1 mA fsd meter is available and we need to measure currents up to 10 mA, a shunt resistor will be required. 1 mA will then pass through the meter and the remaining current 9 mA (10 mA − 1 mA) will pass through the shunt. The value of the shunt resistor will have to be 9 times smaller than the meter resistance, because the shunt carries 9 times the meter current. Suppose the resistance of the meter coil was 75 Ω, then the value of the shunt resistor is $\frac{75}{9}$ = 8.3 Ω.

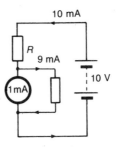

Fig 5.4   Shunt resistor with ammeter

The scale of the meter chosen would read 10 mA (see Fig 5.5), but the full scale deflection of the meter would be 1 mA. In order to read currents up to 10 mA, the meter would have to be used in parallel with an 8.3 Ω shunt.

Fig 5.5   Milliammeter

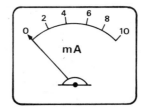

Suppose we wanted to use this 1 mA fsd meter to measure voltages up to 10 volts, then a **series resistor** would be required. The voltmeter would be connected as shown in Fig 5.6a. The voltmeter would consist of a milliammeter and a series resistor R_s. The potential difference across the milliammeter and series resistor R_s is 10 volts. The current through the milliammeter and series resistor must be 1 mA at full scale deflection of the meter.

Fig 5.6 (a) Voltmeter position in circuit   (b) Series resistor with milliammeter

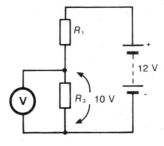 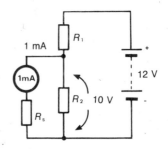

Using Ohm's Law,
$$V = IR$$
$$10 \text{ volts} = 1 \text{ mA} \times R_s$$
$$R_s = \frac{10}{0.001}$$
$$R_s = 10\,000\,\Omega.$$

So, to adapt the 1 mA meter to read up to 10 volts, we would need a 1 kΩ series resistor. The scale of the meter could be calibrated to read from 0 to 10 volts as shown in Fig 5.7, although the fsd is still 1 mA.

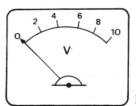

Fig 5.7   Voltmeter

□ Measuring Current and Voltage with a Multimeter

Moving coil milliammeters and microammeters can be used to measure currents and voltages. One measuring instrument, called a **multimeter**, can be used to measure currents, voltages and resistance. Fig 5.8 shows a typical multimeter that could be used for the measurements.

The correct range for the required measurement is selected by turning the central pointer on the front of the multimeter. The value of current, voltage or resistance is read from the appropriate scale of the multimeter (see Fig 5.8). Test leads can be attached to the multimeter at the terminals marked positive (+) and negative (−). These are connected to the appropriate position in the circuit.

Fig 5.8   Multimeter

☐ Measuring Resistance with a Multimeter

The multimeter can be used to measure resistance. The resistance range of the multimeter may give several multiplier values of resistance R, such as $R \times 1$, $R \times 10$, $R \times 100$ and $R \times 1000$. If you wanted to measure the resistance value of a component, you would select the multiplier range which allowed an easy reading from the ohms scale (with the pointer near the centre of the scale).

In order to measure the resistance of a component, it must be placed in a circuit with a power supply (battery), a meter, a fixed resistor and a variable resistor.

Fig 5.9 (a)   Multimeter used to measure resistance   (b)   Ohmmeter circuit

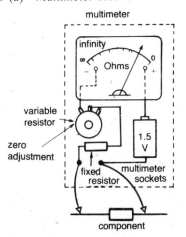

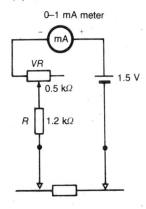

57

The ohmmeter circuit (see Fig 5.9), inside the multimeter, consists of a cell or battery, a variable resistor *VR*, a fixed resistor *R* and a meter (perhaps 1 mA fsd), all connected in series. To measure the resistance of a component, select the required ohms range, join the ends of the test leads together (as in Fig 5.10) and adjust the variable resistor *VR* until the meter reads full scale. This is zero ohms. The zero of the scale is at the right-hand end of the scale. With the test leads touched together, a current flows in the ohmmeter circuit and causes a full deflection of the meter.

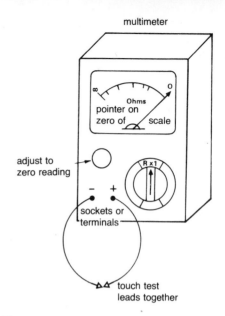

Fig 5.10 Setting the multimeter at zero on the ohms scale

The ohm scale reads from right to left as shown in Fig 5.11. Zero ohms is on the right and very large resistance values, up to infinity, on the left.

Fig 5.11 Ohms scale of multimeter

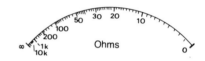

When the test leads are separated, no current flows in the ohmmeter circuit and the meter reads the air gap between the ends of the leads as an infinitely high resistance. If the test leads are now connected to a component, as shown in Fig 5.12, then the meter will show an intermediate resistance. Since the meter scale is calibrated in ohms, the resistance value of the component can be read from the scale.

Fig 5.12 Measuring resistance of component with multimeter

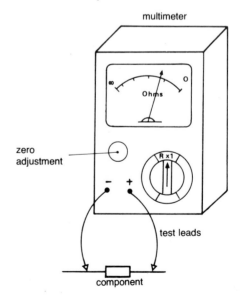

■ The Thermistor

We have already met one special kind of resistor, the LDR. You will recall that the light-dependent resistor has a low resistance in bright sunlight and a high resistance in the dark.

1 How could you measure the resistance of an LDR?
2 Which photographic instrument uses this principle?

A special kind of resistor, which has a resistance that varies with temperature, is called a **thermistor**. The thermistor is made of a semiconducting material. The most common thermistors are made of a material that decreases in resistance as the temperature rises. Fig 5.13 shows two kinds of thermistor, the disc and the glass bead thermistor.

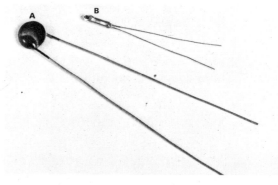

Fig 5.13 (a) Disc thermistor (b) Glass bead thermistor

3 How could you measure the temperature dependence of a thermistor?

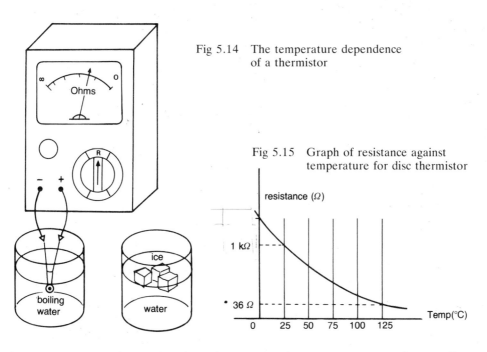

Fig 5.14 The temperature dependence of a thermistor

Fig 5.15 Graph of resistance against temperature for disc thermistor

Fig. 5.15 shows a graph of resistance against temperature for a disc thermistor.

59

Notice the graph is not linear (not a straight line), and it has a negative gradient. The resistance falls rapidly as the temperature increases. Thermistors are used for temperature measurement, switching and control applications.

The circuit diagram symbol for a thermistor is shown in Fig 5.16.

Fig 5.16   Circuit diagram symbol for thermistor

■ Design Problem: An Ice Alarm

Suppose we had to design an alarm system to warn people that the temperature outside had reached freezing point (0°C). The alarm could be used by motorists or horticulturists to warn them of freezing conditions outside.

Alarm systems usually require some form of visual or audible warning device similar to that shown in Fig 5.17. In order to sense the fall in temperature we will use a thermistor. Automatic switching will be required and this can be achieved with a transistor switching circuit.

Fig 5.17   Audible warning device

Fig 5.18 shows a block diagram of a possible solution to the ice alarm problem.

Fig 5.18   Block diagram of ice alarm system

| sensor of cold (thermistor) | → | transistor switching circuit | → | interface device (relay) | → | audible warning device (buzzer) |

The thermistor could be used with a variable resistor to form a potential divider network to bias a transistor. The resistance change in the thermistor could be used to switch the transistor. Fig 5.19 shows a method of using the thermistor to bias a transistor to turn a lightbulb on.

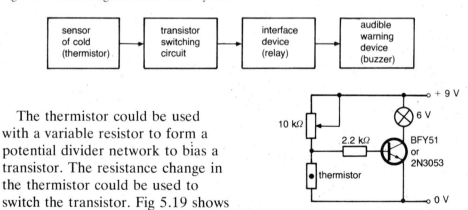

Fig 5.19   Thermistor used to bias simple transistor switch (sensing cold)

The addition of an extra transistor will produce a more sensitive circuit. The lightbulb would have to be replaced by a relay to operate the 12 V audible warning device. The complete ice alarm system is shown in Fig 5.20.

60

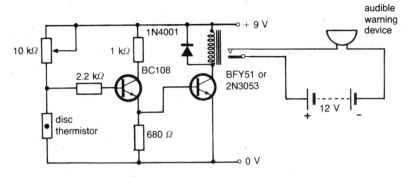

Fig 5.20   Ice alarm system

The ice alarm circuit could be modified for temperature control applications. For example, you could probably design a system to turn a heater on and off in a greenhouse as the temperature fell at night. This would also be an example of an on/off automatic control.

■ Design Problem: A Fire Alarm

Suppose we had to design a fire alarm system that would automatically turn on a solenoid valve controlling water sprinklers, if the temperature in a store rises above about 100°C.

A solenoid valve consists of a disc valve attached by a rod to a ferrous core. The valve is held in a closed position by a spring pressing the core and disc against the valve seating. When a current is passed through the solenoid coil, the core is pulled into the centre of the coil. The valve disc is pulled upward against the force of the spring and water can flow through the valve (see Fig 5.21).

Fig 5.21   Solenoid valve

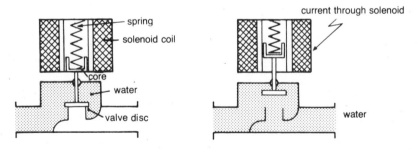

The solenoid valve could operate from a 24 V power supply. We can detect the rise in temperature in the store with a thermistor. When the temperature reaches a certain level, say 100°C, the solenoid valve could be switched on by a transistor switching circuit. Since the transistor circuit works from a 9 V battery and the solenoid valve requires 24 V, a relay could be used to couple the primary and secondary circuits. Fig 5.22 shows a block diagram of the proposed solution for the fire alarm system.

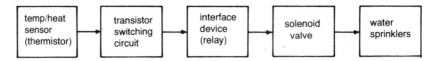

Fig 5.22   Block diagram of fire alarm system

The resistance of a thermistor decreases as the temperature rises. The thermistor and a variable resistor could be used as a potential divider to bias a transistor. A simple transistor switching circuit for turning a lightbulb on is shown in Fig 5.23.

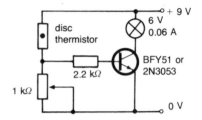

Fig 5.23   Using a thermistor to bias a simple transistor switch (sensing heat)

A more sensitive circuit is produced by the addition of an extra transistor. A complete fire alarm system is shown in Fig 5.24.

Fig 5.24   Complete fire alarm system

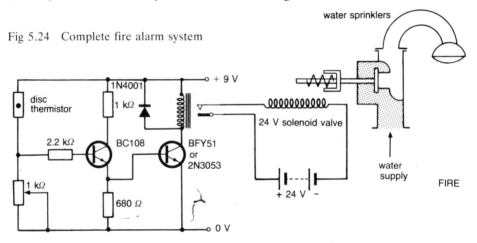

Answers to Questions
1 You could connect the test leads of a multimeter to the LDR and, using the ohm scale, measure its resistance in the dark and in bright sunlight.
2 A light meter.
3 Use a multimeter connected to the thermistor and measure its resistance in boiling water and melting ice.

6 Time-delay Circuits

■ Capacitors

In Section 1 you saw that the flow of electrons in a conductor is called an electric current and electrons have a **negative** electric **charge** so, when electrons flow, negative electric charge flows. The quantity of electric charge is measured in **coulombs**. When one coulomb of charge flows in 1 second, we have an electric current of 1 ampere, i.e. 1 amp = 1 coulomb per second.

It is possible to store electric charge in a circuit with a component called a **capacitor**. The larger the capacitor, the more charge it can store. A capacitor consists of two metal plates, separated by an insulating material (see Fig 6.1).

Fig 6.1 (a)   Capacitor (two flat metal plates)   (b)   Capacitor with insulating material

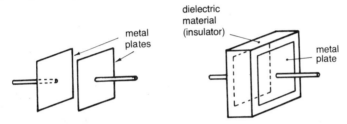

The insulating material between the metal plates is called a **dielectric material**. Several different types of insulating material are used for capacitors, such as paper, polypropylene, polystyrene, polyester, mica and ceramic materials. Even dry air between the metal plates will act as a dielectric material.

The circuit diagram symbol for a capacitor consists of two bars to indicate the flat metal plates (see Fig 6.2).

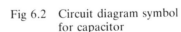

Fig 6.2   Circuit diagram symbol for capacitor

If the leads of a capacitor are connected to a cell or battery, the capacitor will store a charge. The voltage across the capacitor causes a deficiency of electrons on one plate (A) and a surplus of electrons on the other plate (B) (see Fig 6.3).

Fig 6.3   Capacitor connected to cell

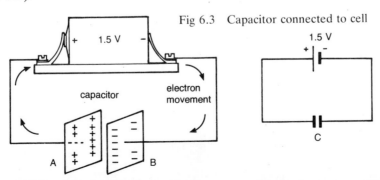

The surplus electrons that collect on plate B give it a negative charge. Electrons flowing from plate A into the cell cause a deficiency of electrons on plate A. This loss of electrons leaves plate A with a positive charge. While the electrons are collecting on the capacitor plate, the capacitor is said to be **charging**. The charging process takes a short period of time. The capacitor is fully charged when the voltage across the plates is the same as the cell or battery voltage.

Notice that no direct current can pass across the plates of the capacitor because they are separated by an insulating material. The ability to store a charge of electricity, the fact that it takes time for this to happen, makes the capacitor a useful electronic component.

■ The Water Analogy and Capacitors

Earlier, we used a water analogy to explain electric current, voltage and resistance. The flow of water in a pipe due to the difference in water levels in two tanks was compared to potential difference in a circuit (voltage across a component). A restriction in a water pipe was compared with a resistor. We can use the water analogy to explain the action of a capacitor.

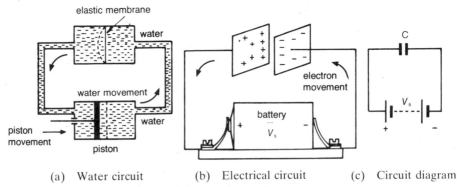

(a)   Water circuit   (b)   Electrical circuit   (c)   Circuit diagram

Fig 6.4   Water analogy used to explain capacitor action

You could compare the capacitor with a water tank in a closed pipework circuit (see Fig 6.4). The dielectric insulating material between the metal plates of the capacitor is like having an elastic membrane across the water tank. No water can pass through the elastic membrane but it can stretch. The water tank is connected to a piston pump and this can be compared with the battery in an electrical circuit. The pressure in the water circuit is created by moving the piston into the pump. Pressure in the water pipe makes the membrane stretch, as shown in Fig 6.4. This can be compared with charging up the capacitor, the larger the water pressure the more the membrane is stretched and the more energy it stores. In an electrical circuit, the larger the battery voltage, the larger is the quantity of electrons (negative charge) stored in the capacitor and the more energy it stores.

If the piston is released, the energy stored in the stretched membrane will cause the water to flow clockwise and push the piston back to its original position. This is like discharging the capacitor. If the applied voltage in an electrical circuit is removed, the capacitor can release stored energy. The voltage across the capacitor plates that was developed when the capacitor charged up, is able to produce electron movement (a current) away from the capacitor. The capacitor is said to discharge.

In the electrical circuit (Fig 6.4c) there is no current flow across the capacitor because there is an insulator, or a gap, between the metal plates. Electrons can only be transferred from one plate to the other around the external circuit by the voltage set up across the plates.

1 What is the maximum voltage that can occur across the plates of the capacitor?

■ Capacitance

The charge-storing ability of a capacitor is called its **capacitance (C)**. The larger the capacitance of the capacitor, the larger the charge it can store. This is rather like a water tank, the larger the capacity of the tank, the larger the amount of water that can be stored. Capacitance is measured in **farads (F)**. The unit is named after Michael Faraday, a British physicist responsible for much of the pioneering work in electricity. The farad is a large unit of capacitance and it is more usual to use a unit which is $\frac{1}{1\,000\,000}$ th of a farad, this is the **microfarad (μF)**. 1 000 000 μF = 1 F.

The **nanofarad (nF)** is used to measure even smaller capacitances. 1000 nF = 1 μF, so 1 000 000 000 nF = 1 F.

The **picofarad (pF)** is used to measure very small capacitances. There are 1 000 000 pF in 1 μF, so 1 000 000 000 000 pF = 1 F.

2 Put the following values of capacitance in ascending order (the smallest first – up to the largest): 100 μF, 100 pF, 10 pF, 10 μF, 10 nF.

■ Types of Capacitor

Small value capacitors (with capacitance values less than 1 μF) can be connected either way round in the circuit. The capacitor shown in Fig 6.5 is an example; its symbol is also shown.

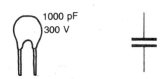

1000 pF
300 V

Fig 6.5 (a) Small value capacitor (b) Circuit diagram symbol

The maximum voltage that can be connected across a capacitor is called its **working voltage**. If the working voltage is exceeded, the capacitor will break

65

down and become useless. Small value capacitors can usually withstand quite high voltages. Working voltages of 250 V dc, even 750 V dc, are common.

These capacitors tend to have preferred values like the following: 0.01 μF, 0.022 μF, 0.047 μF, 0.1 μF, 0.22 μF, 0.47 μF and 1.0 μF.

A variety of materials is used to make these capacitors, some examples are shown in Fig 6.6.

Fig 6.6   Small capacitors.

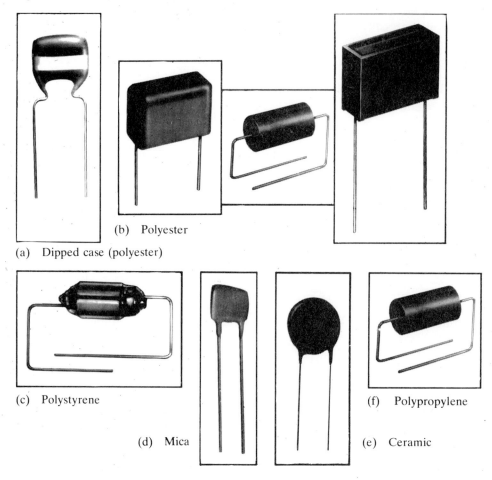

(a)   Dipped case (polyester)

(b)   Polyester

(c)   Polystyrene

(d)   Mica

(e)   Ceramic

(f)   Polypropylene

When larger value capacitances are required, it is normal to use an **electrolytic capacitor**. These capacitors are shaped in a can or tube form (see Fig 6.7).

The tubular form of electrolytic capacitor is made in a printed circuit form with two leads at one end. Electrolytic capacitors work because an oxide is formed by electrolytic action when they are used in a circuit. The voltage applied to an electrolytic capacitor must be of the correct polarity (positive

66

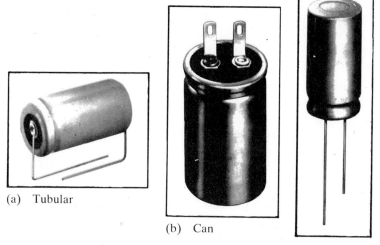

(a) Tubular

(b) Can

Fig 6.7 Electrolytic capacitors

(c) Printed circuit

end of the capacitor towards the positive terminal of the battery in the circuit). These capacitors are marked with a (+ve) positive sign at the necked end (see Fig 6.8a).

The circuit diagram symbol for an electrolytic capacitor is also marked with a positive (+ve) open bar (see Fig 6.8b). Electrolytic capacitors tend to be values larger than 1 μF. Typical preferred values of electrolytic capacitors are: 10 μF, 22 μF, 47 μF, 100 μF, 220 μF, 470 μF, 1000 μF and 2200 μF.

When an electrolytic capacitor is used in a circuit, the positive end of the capacitor is connected towards the most positive part of the circuit, such as the positive terminal of the battery (see Fig 6.9).

Fig 6.8 Electrolytic capacitor
(a) Positive end marked

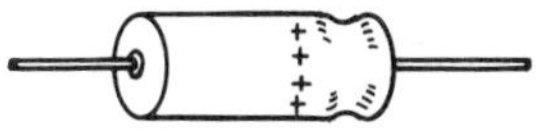

(b) Circuit diagram symbol

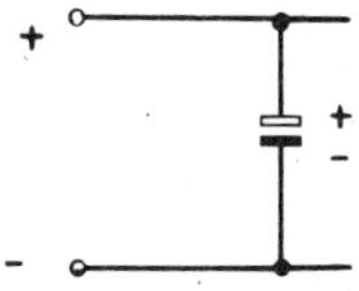

Fig 6.9 Connections for electrolytic capacitor in circuit

Design Problem: A Time-delay Circuit

Time-delay circuits are quite often required for applications like egg-timers or photographic timers, and to produce a time sequence in a control process. Egg-timers and photographic timers can be set for a period of seconds or minutes, and then a warning light might flash on and off or an audible warning device might be sounded. A timing device might be used to turn the garage light off after you have come inside the house. A similar application for a time switch could be to control the electric light in the central hallway of a block of flats. When a person switches on the hall light, a time delay is activated which allows sufficient time for the person to reach his flat before the light automatically turns off. A time delay might be connected to a solenoid in order to close a door or a valve after a predetermined time.

The transistor switching circuit, which we have used in previous lessons, can be modified to work as a time delay by the addition of a capacitor. If a resistor is connected in series with an electrolytic capacitor, it could be used as a time-dependent potential divider to bias a transistor. A simple time-delay circuit is shown in Fig 6.10.

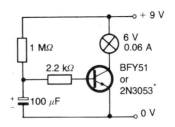

Fig 6.10   Simple time-delay circuit

This circuit would provide a time delay of about 30 seconds. As soon as the battery leads are connected to the battery, the capacitor will start to charge up. When the voltage across the base/emitter junction of the transistor reaches about 0.6 volts, the transistor will begin to conduct and the lightbulb will remain 'on'. If we discharge the capacitor by connecting both ends of it down to the ground rail (0 V), the lightbulb will go 'off'. A method of doing this is to put a single-pole two-way switch in the circuit and make one connection a short circuit round the capacitor. Fig 6.11 shows how a switch will produce an on/off time delay.

When the switch is put in the 'off' position, point A in the circuit is connected to the ground rail, so it is at 0 volts. If point A is at 0 volts, then the base of the transistor is also at 0 volts and the lightbulb is 'off'. Turn the switch to the 'on' position and the capacitor starts to charge up through the 1 MΩ

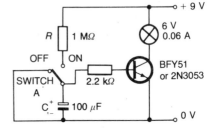

Fig 6.11   'On/Off' time-delay circuit

resistor. When the base of the transistor reaches a point when its potential difference is 0.6 volts higher than the emitter (ground voltage), the transistor begins to conduct. A collector/emitter current flows through the transistor and the lightbulb turns 'on'.

The circuit shown in Fig 6.11 will always provide the same time delay. The time delay is determined by the values of the resistor R and the capacitor C. We could adjust the time delay period by altering the value of the capacitor. For example, the approximate time delays are shown in the table.

68

Capacitor	Time Delay (approx)
100 μF	30 secs
220 μF	45 secs
470 μF	1 min 35 secs
1000 μF	4 mins

Capacitors have quite large tolerances, e.g. 100 μF capacitor can have a tolerance of +80% to −20% so the value could be between 180 μF and 80 μF. It is impossible to state an accurate time delay.

If a variable resistor was used instead of the fixed 1 MΩ resistor, it would be possible to adjust the time period. The circuit shown in Fig 6.12 can be adjusted for time delays between 0 and 30 seconds.

The sensitivity of the time delay circuit can be improved by the addition of an extra transistor. This circuit is shown in Figs 6.13 and 6.14.

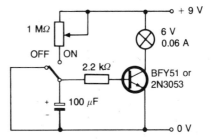

Fig 6.12   Adjustable time-delay circuit

Fig 6.13   Improved time-delay circuit

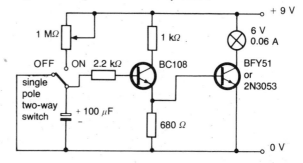

Fig 6.14   Complete time-delay circuit

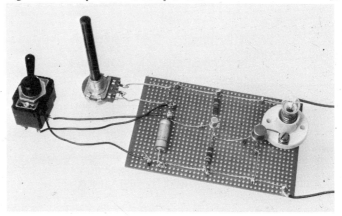

Answers to Questions
1 The battery voltage V_s.
2 10 pF, 100 pF, 10 nF, 10 μF, 100 μF.

ADDITIONAL NOTES

Charge on Capacitors

In a capacitor, the property that determines the quantity of charge Q that can be stored for a given potential difference V, applied to the plates, is the capacitance C. The ratio of charge Q to potential difference V is called capacitance C.

$$C = \frac{Q}{V}$$

Capacitance C is measured in farads (F).
Charge Q is measured in coulombs (C).
Potential difference V is measured in volts (V).

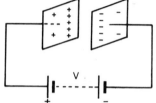

Fig 6.15   Charge on a capacitor

Example
How much charge can be stored on a $1000\,\mu$F capacitor if it is charged up by a 10 V battery?

Using $C = \dfrac{Q}{V}$,

$$Q = CV$$

$$\therefore Q = \frac{1000 \times 10}{1\,000\,000} \text{ coulombs}$$

(Remember 1 μF is $\dfrac{1}{1\,000\,000}$ th of a farad.)

$$Q = \frac{10}{1000} \text{ coulomb}$$

$\therefore$ Charge $Q = 0.01$ coulomb.

The capacitance of a capacitor is dependent on the area A of the plates and the distance d between the plates. Area A is measured in square metres and distance d is measured in metres. The capacitance is proportional to the area A divided by distance d.

$$C \propto \frac{A}{d}$$

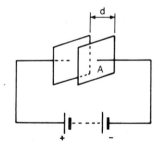

Fig 6.16   Capacitor plates

$$C = \varepsilon \frac{A}{d} \quad (\varepsilon \text{ is called the permittivity of the dielectric material})$$

Charging and Discharging the Capacitor

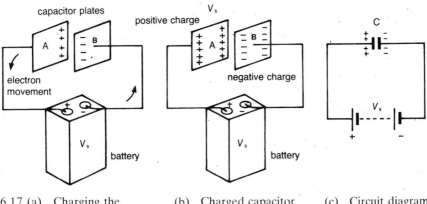

Fig 6.17 (a)   Charging the capacitor   (b) Charged capacitor   (c) Circuit diagram

If a capacitor is connected to a battery, the capacitor will begin to charge up. The battery (voltage V_s) acts as a driving force to move electrons on to plate B, as shown in Fig 6.17a. The electrons have a negative charge, so plate B gradually becomes negatively charged. The loss of electrons from the negative terminal of the battery means that the overall number of electrons in the battery is maintained by electrons moving from plate A of the capacitor. A deficiency of electrons on plate A leaves it positively charged. (Remember atoms are electrically neutral; they have equal numbers of electrons (−ve charge) and protons (+ve charge). If electrons are removed, the remaining atom is positively charged.)

Eventually, the number of electrons on plate B is sufficient to repel any more electrons and the capacitor is fully charged (see Fig 6.17b). When the capacitor is charged, the voltage between the plates is at a maximum value. This voltage value depends on the applied voltage of the battery V_s.

After a short period of time the capacitor is fully charged. At first the voltage between the plates rises rapidly but it then slows down. Fig 6.18 shows a graph of capacitor voltage against time. The curve of the rising voltage is an inverted exponential shape.

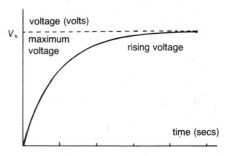

Fig 6.18   Graph of voltage against time for charging capacitor

You could demonstrate this capacitor charging effect by using the circuit shown in Fig 6.19. A resistor, switch, capacitor and battery are placed in series. The rising voltage across the capacitor can be displayed on a voltmeter or on an oscilloscope. (An oscilloscope is a special kind of voltmeter, with a visual display on a cathode-ray tube). When the switch is closed, the voltage across the capacitor makes the voltmeter needle move quickly at first and then slow down. If an oscilloscope is used to display the voltage rise of a charging capacitor, the time/cm, or time base, will need to be on a slow scan. The speed at which the spot on the oscilloscope screen moves from left to right is controlled by the setting of the **time/cm** or **time base** switch.

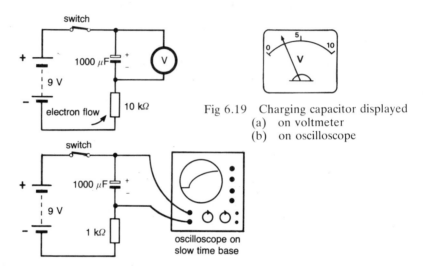

Fig 6.19   Charging capacitor displayed
(a)   on voltmeter
(b)   on oscilloscope

If the battery is disconnected from the circuit and the leads are touched together, the capacitor will discharge through the resistor (see Fig 6.20).

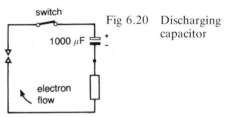

Fig 6.20   Discharging capacitor

Fig 6.21 shows a graph of the capacitor voltage against time for a discharging capacitor. This graph is exponential in shape. The capacitor discharge could be displayed on the voltmeter or oscilloscope.

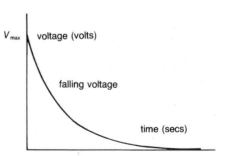

Fig 6.21   Graph of voltage against time for discharging capacitor

Time Constant

When a capacitor is charging up, the voltage rises to a maximum value of almost the supply voltage V_s (see Fig 6.22).

The time taken for the capacitor voltage to rise to about $\frac{2}{3}$ of its maximum voltage, is called the **time constant**. In a circuit containing a resistor and a capacitor in series, the time constant is the product of capacitance C and resistance R:
time constant $(t) = CR$ where time constant (t) is in seconds, capacitance C is in farads and resistance R is in ohms.

It takes about five time constants t for the capacitor to charge up to its maximum voltage V_{max} (see Fig 6.23).

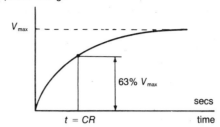

Fig 6.22 Time constant for charging capacitor

Fig 6.23 Time constants required to reach maximum voltage

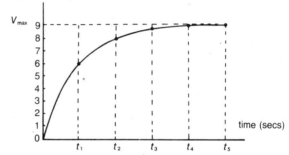

Example 1
Find the time constant for a circuit containing a capacitor 1000 μF and a resistor 10 kΩ (see Fig 6.19a).

Time constant $t = CR$
$$t = \frac{1000}{1\ 000\ 000} \times 10\ 000$$
$$t = 10 \text{ seconds}$$
∴ time constant is 10 seconds.

Example 2
Find the time constant for a circuit containing a capacitor 1000 μF and a resistor 1 kΩ (see Fig 6.19b).

Time constant $t = CR$
$$t = \frac{1000}{1\ 000\ 000} \times 1000$$
$$t = 1 \text{ second}$$
∴ time constant is 1 second.

73

7 Multivibrator Circuits

☐ Using Capacitors: Series and Parallel Connections

Sometimes when you are building a circuit, you will find that capacitors need to be combined to produce a larger or smaller capacitance.

Suppose you wanted to produce a capacitance of 200 μF, you could use two capacitors of value 100 μF connected in parallel as shown in Fig 7.1.

If you wanted a capacitance of 50 μF, two capacitors of value 100 μF could be connected in series as shown in Fig 7.2.

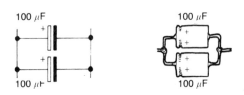

Fig 7.1   Capacitors connected in parallel

Fig 7.2   Capacitors connected in series

When capacitors are connected in parallel, their capacitance values are added together. The formula for capacitors connected in parallel is:

$C = C_1 + C_2 \ldots C_n$

Example 1

What is the combined capacitance of two 100 μF capacitors connected in parallel?

Using $C = C_1 + C_2$,

$\qquad C = 100 \ \mu F + 100 \ \mu F = 200 \ \mu F.$

Combined capacitance is 200 μF.

When capacitors are connected in series, the reciprocals of their capacitance values are added. The formula for capacitors connected in series is:

$$\frac{1}{C} = \frac{1}{C_1} + \frac{1}{C_2} \ldots \frac{1}{C_n}$$

Example 2

What is the combined capacitance of two 100 μF capacitors connected in series?

Using $\dfrac{1}{C} = \dfrac{1}{C_1} + \dfrac{1}{C_2}$,

$$\frac{1}{C} = \frac{1}{100} + \frac{1}{100} = \frac{1 + 1}{100} = \frac{2}{100}$$

$$C = \frac{100}{2} = 50\,\mu F.$$

Combined capacitance is $50\,\mu F$.

Example 3
What is the combined capacitance of capacitors of value 680 pF, 220 pF and 100 pF when connected in parallel?

Using $C = C_1 + C_2 + C_3$,

$\qquad C = 680 + 220 + 100$ pF

$\qquad C = 1000$ pF.

1000 pF is the same as 1 nF or 0.001 μF.

∴ Combined capacitance is 1000 pF or 1 nF or 0.001 μF.

Example 4
What is the combined capacitance of capacitors of value 100 pF and 150 pF connected in series?

Using $\dfrac{1}{C} = \dfrac{1}{C_1} + \dfrac{1}{C_2}$

$$\frac{1}{C} = \frac{1}{100} + \frac{1}{150} = \frac{3+2}{300} = \frac{5}{300}$$

$$C = \frac{300}{5} = 60\ \text{pF}.$$

∴ Combined capacitance is 60 pF.

■ Design Problem: An Electronic Egg-timer

Suppose we wanted to design an electronic egg-timer. The time it takes to boil an egg is about four minutes. This depends on the size and freshness of the egg, and on whether the egg is put in a pan of cold water and brought to the boil and then timed, or if the egg is put into boiling water and then timed. Some people like their boiled egg very soft, while others like the egg to be well done.

ALTERNATIVE DESIGNS →

Fig 7.3   The electronic egg-timer

Let us assume that the egg will take up to four minutes if it is initially put into boiling water. We require an electronic system consisting of a four-minute time delay and an audible or visual warning device. Fig 7.4 shows a block diagram of such an electronic system.

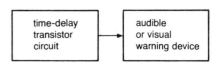

Fig 7.4   Block diagram of electronic egg-timer system

You will have already made a time-delay circuit in Activity 6 in your workbook. The egg-timer will require an adjustable time delay up to four minutes. Fig 7.5 shows a suitable circuit that was built in the second assignment of Activity 6.

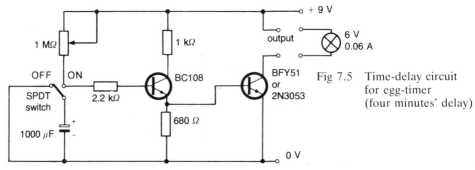

Fig 7.5   Time-delay circuit for egg-timer (four minutes' delay)

To attract the cook's attention when the set time has elapsed, a visual or audible warning device is required. You can choose which circuit to build, either a flashing light circuit or a buzzer circuit. Both warning devices use the same type of switching circuit called an **astable multivibrator**. The circuit will vibrate 'on' and 'off' and will never be in one stable position.

Flashing lights are much better for attracting your attention than a light which is 'on' continuously. If we use a transistor to switch a lightbulb 'on' and 'off', then a flashing light circuit will require two transistors and two light-bulbs. A suitable flashing light circuit is shown in Fig 7.6.

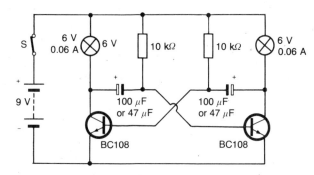

Fig 7.6 Flashing light circuit (astable multivibrator)

The lamps flash alternately. When one lamp is 'off' the other lamp is 'on'. The rate at which the lamps flash 'on' and 'off' is determined by the value of the capacitors and resistors in the circuit. If you increase the value of the capacitors or resistors, the lamps will flash more slowly. If the capacitor values or resistor values are decreased, then the lamps will flash more quickly.

1 *If 47 μF capacitors were used in the flashing light circuit shown in Fig 7.6 instead of the 100 μF capacitors, what effect would it have on the circuit performance?*

It is more common to alter the resistance values of the circuit than to change the capacitors, which involves unnecessary soldering. The resistance can be adjusted by putting a variable resistor or a preset resistor in the circuit. An adjustable flashing light circuit is shown in Fig 7.7.

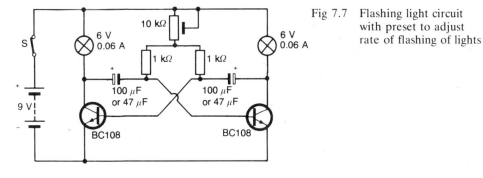

Fig 7.7 Flashing light circuit with preset to adjust rate of flashing of lights

A variable resistor is adjusted by a control knob (see Fig 7.8a). A preset resistor is adjusted by inserting a small screwdriver in a slot cut in the centre wiper control. This wiper moves over a carbon resistance track in a similar way to the variable resistor (see Fig 7.8b). The advantage of using a preset in this circuit is that it costs less than variable resistors, takes up less space and cannot be accidentally altered.

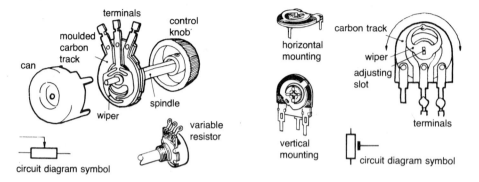

Fig 7.8 (a) Variable resistor   (b) Preset resistor

An audible warning device can be made by modification of the astable multivibrator circuit. If the lightbulbs are replaced by resistors and lower value capacitors are used, then the switching 'on' and 'off' of the transistors can be used as a buzzer circuit. Fig 7.9 shows a buzzer circuit that could be used as the electronic egg-timer warning device. This circuit uses a cheap telephone earpiece as a loudspeaker.

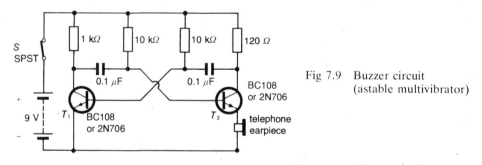

Fig 7.9 Buzzer circuit (astable multivibrator)

The telephone earpiece contains a magnet and a small wire coil. There is less chance of damaging transistor T_2 if the earpiece is placed in the emitter circuit. You could build the multivibrator circuit with the earpiece in the collector circuit (see Fig 7.10). It is suggested that a series resistor is used with

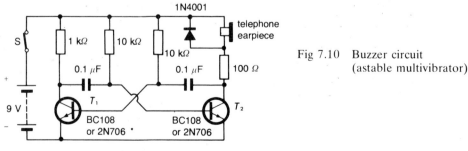

Fig 7.10 Buzzer circuit (astable multivibrator)

78

the earpiece. (A telephone earpiece has a working resistance, called its 'impedance', of about 30 ohms.) It is essential to put a diode across the earpiece to protect the transistors from back voltages.

The buzzer circuit works in a similar way to the flashing light circuit. The transistors are alternately 'on' and 'off'. When transistor T_1 is not conducting, the transistor T_2 is conducting. The current through the collector circuit of the transistors is continually increasing and decreasing. This produces a buzzer sound from the telephone earpiece.

 The pitch of the sound produced by the buzzer circuit can be altered with different value resistors or capacitors. For example, to give a higher note the capacitor values could be decreased to $0.047\,\mu\mathrm{F}$ or $0.01\,\mu\mathrm{F}$. A lower note is produced by larger value capacitors, such as $0.22\,\mu\mathrm{F}$ or $0.47\,\mu\mathrm{F}$.

Fig 7.11   Complete audible warning device (buzzer circuit)

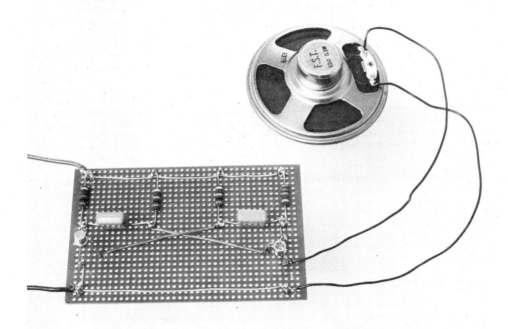

2 *What kind of sound will the buzzer circuit earpiece produce with larger capacitors, such as 4.7 μF?*

Two different kinds of warning device have been described. A flashing-light circuit is a visual warning device. A buzzer circuit is an audible warning device. Either of these warning devices could be connected to the time-delay circuit output to give an electronic egg-timer. The complete egg-timer circuits are shown in Fig 7.12 and 7.13. The time delay and the multivibrator circuits use the same battery in this electronic egg-timer.

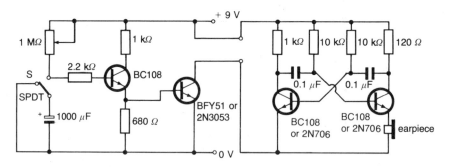

Fig 7.12 Electronic egg-timer (audible warning device)

Fig 7.13 Electronic egg-timer (visual warning device)

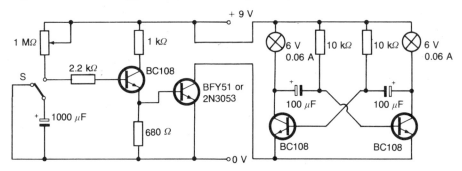

☐ **Multivibrator Circuit Modifications and Applications**

Red Flashing Light
The astable multivibrator can be used as a visual warning device to alert people's attention to danger. The flashing light circuit could be used as an accident warning device beside a motor vehicle accident. The circuit could be used as a visual alarm in an industrial processing plant. It could warn the operator that the process was not working properly, perhaps because of overheating or lack of fuel. You could use a flashing light circuit to remind the motorist that he had not fastened his seatbelt or that he had left his sidelights on after leaving the car. The circuit might be used on a model railway as level-crossing lights.

In these applications it would be better to have red flashing lights. The lightbulb and holder in previous circuits could be replaced by a **light emitting diode (LED)**. This is a special kind of diode that gives out light rather like a lightbulb. The LED is made from a semiconducting material called gallium arsenide phosphide.

80

The LED will emit light when a small current is passed through it, usually about 10 mA. Like all diodes, the LED will only allow current to pass through the diode in one direction. A light-emitting diode is shown in Fig 7.14.

Fig 7.14 (a) Light emitting diode (LED)   (b) Circuit diagram symbol for LED

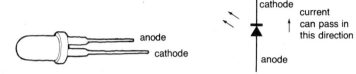

Current can only flow through the LED from the **anode** to the **cathode**. The cathode lead is determined by the longer lead or by a flat marked on the body of the LED. The voltage across the LED is usually about 2 volts. If the LED is to be used in our multivibrator circuit, a series resistor will be required to avoid damaging it with a large current. It is possible to obtain red, yellow or green LEDs. Fig 7.15 shows a flashing LED circuit that could be used as a danger warning device.

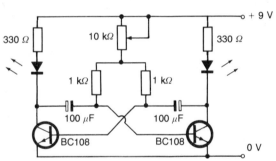

Fig 7.15   Flashing LED circuit (astable multivibrator)

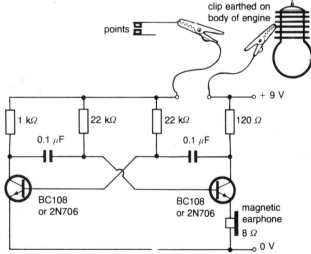

Kart Timing Device
The audible multivibrator circuit can be used as an indication device for setting the timing on a kart (go-kart). The buzzer circuit will change its output note when the kart contact-breaker points are just open. In order to adjust the timing on a kart, it is necessary to know the exact time when the points are open. A suitable circuit is shown in Fig 7.16.

Fig 7.16   Timing/points setting device (astable multivibrator)

81

Two flying leads with a crocodile clip at one end are connected to the circuit (see Fig 7.16). One of the crocodile clips is attached to one side of the contact points and the other crocodile clip is attached to the body of the kart engine. (This acts as an earthing lead.) It is a good idea to use an earphone, like the one shown in Fig 7.17, in the buzzer circuit.

Even if karts are being tuned up close by, you will still be able to detect a note change as the contact points open. When a battery is connected to the buzzer circuit, a high pitch note can be heard from the earphone. As the engine flywheel is rotated, the contact points open and the note from the earphone will change pitch.

Fig 7.17   Earphone

Electronic Organ

If a suitable loudspeaker is used with the multivibrator circuit, a musical note can be produced. You will recall that the pitch of the note can be altered by changing the values of resistors or capacitors in the multivibrator circuit. It is more practical to have a number of different resistors in the circuit to give a number of notes with varying pitch. If the resistors are presets, the note can be adjusted to give the correct pitch of the notes of a musical scale.

3 Do you know how many notes there are in a major musical scale?
4 What is an octave?
5 How many notes cover an octave on the piano?

Fig 7.18   Electronic organ

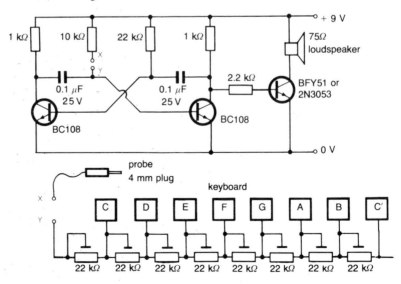

82

The multivibrator circuit is modified by the addition of a transistor (BFY51 or 2N3053) to drive the loudspeaker and a range of preset resistors to give a musical scale. A flying lead with a probe (a 4 mm plug) is connected to point X in the circuit. Point Y in the circuit is connected to eight presets which are joined in series. The presets could be connected to a keyplate, perhaps made from copper-covered laminate board (printed circuit board) or a push button switch. When the probe is touched on to a key plate, a musical note is sounded from the electronic organ. Fine tuning of each note is achieved by adjustment of the preset resistors. The first note can be tuned to middle C of the piano. Fig 7.19 shows the electronic components assembled as an electronic organ.

Fig 7.19   Electronic organ

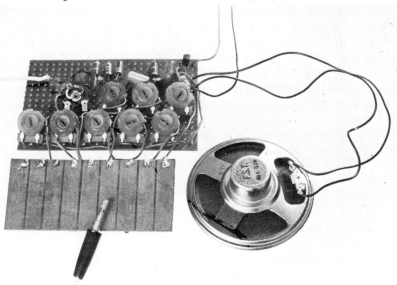

☐ How the Multivibrator Works

To explain how the multivibrator works, we will consider the flashing light form of the multivibrator circuit (see Fig 7.20).

When switch S is closed, the 9 V battery is connected to the multivibrator circuit. Transistor T_1 starts to conduct and lightbulb L_1 turns 'on'. There is now a voltage drop across lightbulb L_1, and the voltage at the collector of transistor T_1 falls (i.e. it goes less positive). Since capacitor C_1 and resistor R_1

Fig 7.20   Flashing light multivibrator circuit

83

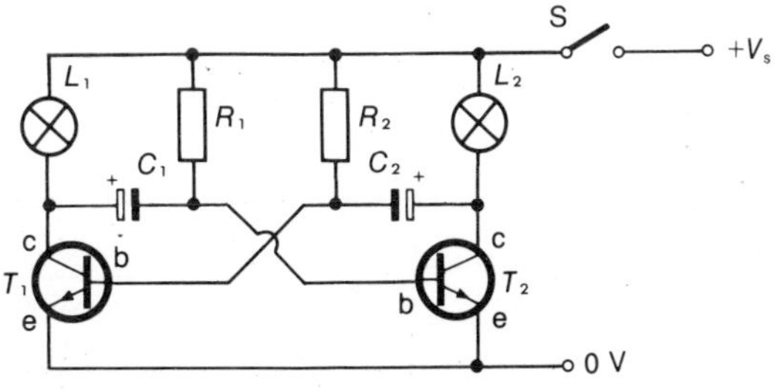

act as a potential divider to bias the transistor T_2, a change in voltage at the collector of T_1 will be reflected to the base of the transistor T_2 by the capacitor C_1. Transistor T_2 begins to turn 'off', so lightbulb L_2 goes out. The voltage at the collector of transistor T_2 starts to rise. Resistor R_2 and capacitor C_2 form a potential divider to bias the base of transistor T_1. The rising voltage at the collector of T_2 is reflected by capacitor C_2 and the base bias voltage of transistor T_1 increases, turning it even fuller 'on'. Lightbulb L_1 is full 'on' and bulb L_2 is 'off'.

This situation cannot last. Current flows through resistor R_1 and begins to charge up capacitor C_1. The voltage at the base of transistor T_2 starts to rise (remember capacitor C_1 and resistor R_1 are a potential divider). When the base voltage of transistor T_2 rises to about 0.6 volts, it begins to conduct. The collector voltage of transistor T_2 falls. Transistor T_1 is driven off through capacitor C_2. The T_1 collector voltage rises, and capacitor C_1 is discharging through transistor T_2. This transistor T_2 is driven full 'on' and so the lightbulb L_2 turns 'on'.

The lamps of the multivibrator flash alternately. When one lamp is 'on' the other is 'off'. The rate at which the lamps flash on and off is determined by the values of capacitor C_1 and resistor R_1, and also the capacitor C_2 and resistor R_2.

6 How could you slow down the rate at which lights flash 'on' and 'off'?

☐ Multivibrator Waveforms

The transistors of the astable multivibrator are alternately conducting and non-conducting. The voltage at the collector of each transistor is alternately rising and falling. Over a period of time, the voltage between the collector and the ground rail is rising to a value of about 5 volts and then falling to 0 volts. If this voltage was displayed on an oscilloscope (a visual form of voltmeter) it would appear as a square castle-shaped trace on the screen. This type of trace is called a **square waveform**. The connection of the oscilloscope to the multivibrator circuit is shown in Fig 7.21. The square waveform can be examined at the collector of transistors T_1 or T_2. This waveform is shown in Fig 7.22.

Fig 7.21   Examining waveform of astable multivibrator using oscilloscope

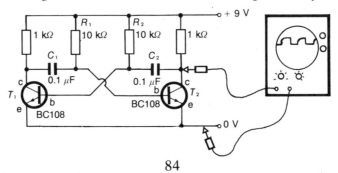

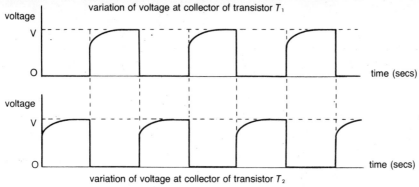

Fig 7.22   Square waveform of astable multivibrator

The square wave trace that appears on the screen of the oscilloscope is like a graph of voltage against time (in seconds). The square peaks that appear in the waveform are called **voltage pulses**. The number of these square wave voltage pulses that occur in one second is called the **frequency** of the waveform. So the frequency of the waveform is the repetition rate of the voltage pulses. Frequency is measured in **Hertz (Hz)** where 1 Hz is 1 pulse per second.

The time that a transistor is 'on' is time period t_1; during time period t_2, the transistor is 'off'. The time for a voltage pulse, that occurs when the transistor is conducting, is called the **mark**. The time between voltage pulses is called the **space**. So the ratio of t_1 to t_2 is called the **mark-space ratio** (see Fig 7.23).

Fig 7.23   Square waveform (mark-space)

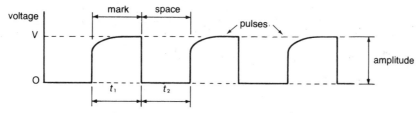

When capacitors C_1 and C_2 are equal and resistors R_1 and R_2 are equal, the mark and the space will be equal. So the mark-space ratio $t_1/t_2 = 1$.

The height of a voltage pulse is called the **amplitude** (see Fig 7.23). The amplitude of a pulse waveform will be measured in volts, because the square waveform is a display of voltage against time.

Answers to Questions
1 The lamps would flash more quickly.
2 Just 'clicks', like a metronome.
3 In a major musical scale there are 7 notes, e.g. for the scale of C major, this would be C, D, E, F, G, A, C̄.
4 The note produced by twice or half the frequency of a given note.
5 An octave consists of 13 notes on the piano: 8 white and 5 black keys.
6 Increase the capacitance value of capacitors C_1 and C_2, or increase the value of resistors R_1 and R_2.

ADDITIONAL NOTES

The Frequency of the Multivibrator

The frequency of the waveform of a multivibrator depends on a factor called the **time constant**. You will recall that time constant $t = CR$ seconds, where C is capacitance in farads and R is resistance in ohms.

Fig 7.24   Cycles of square waveform

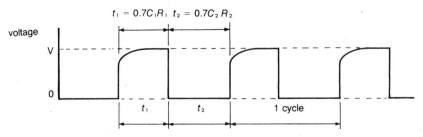

The frequency of the multivibrator is given by the formula: $f = \dfrac{1}{t_1 + t_2}$

where t_1 is the time, transistor T_1 is on and transistor T_2 is off, and t_2 is the time, transistor T_2 is on and transistor T_1 is off. The charging rate of capacitor C_1 is determined by the time constant $C_1 \times R_1$. The charging rate of capacitor C_2 is determined by the time constant $C_2 \times R_2$. The time constant is the time taken for the voltage across the capacitor to rise about $\frac{2}{3}$ of the way between initial voltage and the final voltage. Using a known formula:

$t_1 = 0.7C_1 R_1$ and $t_2 = 0.7C_2 R_2$

then frequency $f = \dfrac{1}{t_1 + t_2} = \dfrac{1}{0.7C_1R_1 + 0.7C_2R_2}$

but C_1 and C_2 are equal in the multivibrator in section 7, and R_1 and R_2 are also equal, so

$$f = \frac{1}{1.4C_1 R_1} \text{ or } \frac{1}{1.4C_2 R_2}$$

Example 1
Calculate the frequency of the multivibrator shown in Fig 7.25.
Capacitor $C_1 = C_2 = 0.1\ \mu F$.
Resistor $R_1 = R_2 = 10\ k\Omega$.
Using the formula:

frequency $f = \dfrac{1}{1.4C_1 \times R_1}$

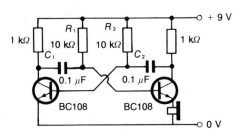

Fig 7.25   Astable multivibrator

86

$$f = \frac{1}{1.4 \times 0.1 \times 10^{-6} \times 10\ 000}$$ (1 microfarad is 10^{-6} farads)

$$f = \frac{10^6}{1.4 \times 0.1 \times 10\ 000} = \frac{1\ 000\ 000}{1.4 \times 0.1 \times 10\ 000}$$

$$f = \frac{1000}{1.4}\text{Hz}$$

$$f = 714.2\ \text{Hz}$$

$\therefore$ Frequency is about 714 Hz.

Example 2
Calculate the frequency of the flashing-light multivibrator shown in Fig 7.26.

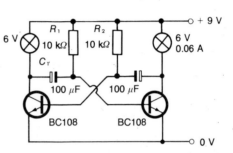

Fig 7.26 Flashing-light multivibrator

Capacitor $C_1 = C_2 = 100\ \mu\text{F}$.
Resistor $R_1 = R_2 = 10\ \text{k}\Omega$.
Using the formula:

$$\text{frequency } f = \frac{1}{1.4C_1 \times R_1}$$

$$f = \frac{1}{1.4 \times 100 \times 10^{-6} \times 10\ 000}$$

$$f = \frac{10^6}{1.4 \times 100 \times 10\ 000} = \frac{1\ 000\ 000}{1.4 \times 100 \times 10\ 000}$$

$$f = \frac{1}{1.4}\ \text{Hz}$$

$$f = 0.714\ \text{Hz}$$

$\therefore$ Frequency is about 0.7 Hz.

8 The Transistor as an Amplifier

■ Introduction

In Activity 3, Assignment 3, you were introduced to the use of a transistor as an amplifier. It was used to improve the sensitivity of a switching circuit. Now you will learn more about the amplifying action of a transistor.

An **amplifier** is a device that magnifies or enlarges its input. The output from an amplifier is a magnified version of the input. A mechanical amplifier might amplify small movements. A small input movement is amplified to a large output movement. Electronic amplifiers magnify small input signals and produce larger output signals. The input to an electronic amplifier might be a voltage or a current.

1 Where have you heard the term 'amplifier' used in everyday life?

Electronic amplifiers need an external source of power. For example, a transistor radio amplifier might use a battery as a source of power, a stereo amplifier might use mains electricity for its power.

To summarise:
  an amplifier has an input and an output;
  an amplifier is a device that magnifies the input signal to produce a larger output signal;
  an electronic amplifier has an external source of power.

Fig 8.1   Block diagram of amplifier

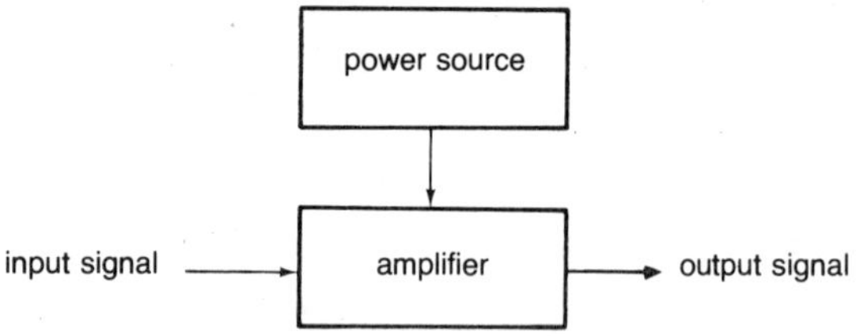

power source

input signal ⟶ amplifier ⟶ output signal

■ The Transistor

Earlier, you made use of the transistor as a switch. The practical circuits you have constructed have been switching circuits. Some of the important results about transistors can be summarised by the diagrams in Fig 8.2.

Fig 8.2   Current flow through a transistor (*n-p-n*)

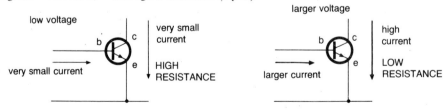

A small base current controls a much larger current flow from collector to emitter through the transistor.

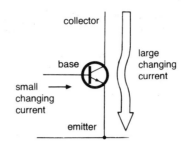

Fig 8.3   Transistor as an amplifier

The transistor acts as an amplifier when the base current changes. A small change in the base current controls a larger current change from the collector to the emitter. The transistor will function as an amplifier.

Electronic engineers are interested in the relationship between collector current and base current, the collector current being controlled by the base current. The ratio of collector current to base current is called the **current gain** of the transistor.

$$\text{Current gain of a transistor} = \frac{\text{collector current}}{\text{base current}}.$$

Example

A transistor has a base current $I_b = 0.1$ mA and a collector current $I_c = 10$ mA. What is the current gain of the transistor?

$$\text{Current gain} = \frac{\text{collector current}}{\text{base current}}$$

$$= \frac{10 \text{ mA}}{0.1 \text{ mA}}$$

∴ Current gain $= 100$.

■ DC Current Gain of a Transistor

Steady currents in one direction are called direct currents (dc). Let us consider the transistor with a steady base current, collector current and emitter current, as shown in Fig 8.4.

The steady base current is I_b. The steady collector current is I_c. The dc gain of the transistor is given by

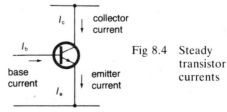

Fig 8.4   Steady transistor currents

$$\frac{\text{collector current}}{\text{base current}} = \frac{I_c}{I_b}$$

The direct current gain is given the symbol h_{FE}

$$\therefore h_{FE} = \frac{\text{collector current}}{\text{base current}}$$

$$h_{FE} = \frac{I_c}{I_b}$$

Example
A transistor has a base current $I_b = 0.1$ mA, a collector current $I_c = 9.9$ mA and an emitter current $I_e = 10$ mA. What is the dc gain of the transistor?

$$h_{FE} = \frac{I_c}{I_b}$$

$$= \frac{9.9 \text{ mA}}{0.1 \text{ mA}}$$

$$\therefore h_{FE} = 99.$$

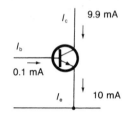

■ Current in a Transistor

The current flowing into a junction equals the current flowing out of the junction. This is a well-known electrical law called **Kirchhoff's First Law**. Since a transistor can be considered as a junction, the current flowing into a transistor equals the current flowing out.

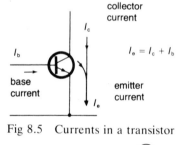

Fig 8.5   Currents in a transistor

So, $I_e = I_c + I_b$.

This could be demonstrated with the circuit shown in Fig 8.6.

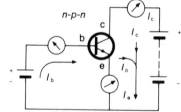

Fig 8.6   Circuit to demonstrate $I_e = I_c + I_b$

Example
In a transistor where the base current $I_b = 0.1$ mA and the collector current $I_c = 9.9$ mA, what is the emitter current I_e?
Using Kirchhoff's First Law,
$I_e = I_c + I_b$
$I_e = 9.9$ mA $+ 0.1$ mA
$\therefore I_e = 10$ mA.

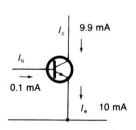

■ Collector and Emitter Current

The base current of a transistor is very small compared with the collector or emitter current. The base current is often less than 5% of the emitter current, so the collector current I_c is actually about 95% of the emitter current I_e. Kirchhoff's First Law states that $I_e = I_c + I_b$. Since I_c is considerably greater than I_b, it is often sufficiently accurate to assume that $I_c = I_e$ (remember that resistors are not accurate anyway and transistor gain can vary).

■ Circuit to Demonstrate the Transistor as an Amplifier

The **amplifying** action of a transistor can be demonstrated using the circuit shown in Fig 8.7 and Fig 8.8. The variable resistor VR_1 can be used to vary the current flow into the base of the transistor. Resistor R_2 ensures that the base current is never too large to damage the transistor.

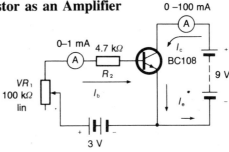

Fig 8.7   Circuit to demonstrate the transistor as an amplifier

Fig 8.8   Practical circuit to demonstrate the amplifying function of a transistor

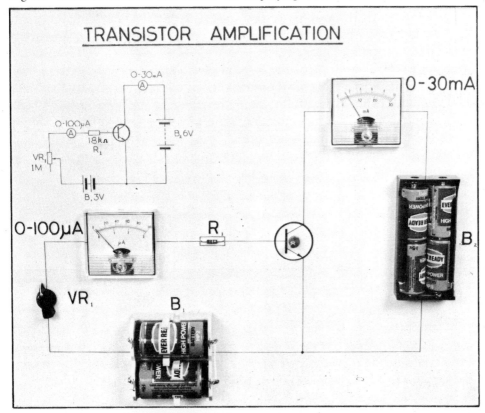

91

Typical figures obtained from this circuit for a BC108 transistor are: as base current I_b changes from 0.02 to 0.06 mA, collector current I_c changes from 8 to 26 mA.

The changing values of base current and collector current show that a change in current is amplified by the transistor. For a transistor with changing direct currents, **current gain** is defined as:

$$\frac{\text{change in collector current}}{\text{change is base current}} \text{ or } h_{fe} = \frac{\Delta I_c}{\Delta I_b} \text{ (Δ represents change).}$$

What is the current gain, h_{fe}, for the typical results obtained for a BC108?

$$h_{fe} = \frac{\Delta I_c}{\Delta I_b} = \frac{26 - 8 \text{ mA}}{0.06 - 0.02 \text{ mA}} = \frac{18}{0.04} = 450.$$

This is a typical figure for a BC108 although values of h_{fe} can vary from 150 to 800 for a range of transistors.

We will assume an average value of 400 in any calculations that are necessary later in the course.

■ Voltage Amplification

Amplifiers are usually used to provide voltage rather than current amplification. Examples of the use of a transistor as a voltage amplifier are in an intercom and a radio circuit.

It is necessary to insert a load resistor in the collector part of the transistor circuit in order to produce an output voltage. Fig 8.9 shows how voltage amplification can be achieved. If a changing voltage is applied as shown to the transistor, this will produce a changing base current which will be amplified by the transistor. This amplified output current passing through the **load resistor** will produce a changing output voltage. The size of the output voltage can be varied by using different values of load resistor.

Fig 8.9   Function of load resistor

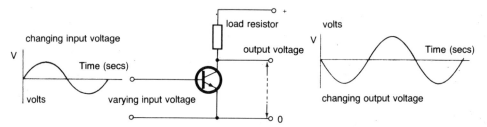

In practice, the process of producing **voltage amplification** is slightly more complicated than this and will be described in detail later.

92

◼ Direct Current (dc) and Alternating Current (ac)

Direct current (dc) flows in one direction round a circuit. The direction of conventional current flow is from the positive end of the conductor towards the negative end.

In the diagram shown in Fig 8.10, the battery causes a direct current to flow from the positive terminal (+ve) towards the negative terminal (−ve).

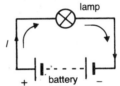

Fig 8.10   Direct current flows in one direction

When a current flows backwards and forwards in a conductor, it is known as an **alternating current** (**ac**). An alternating current increases from zero to maximum value, falls to zero again and then reverses, following an identical pattern in the opposite direction. Fig 8.11 shows a graph of alternating current (*i*) against time.

Fig 8.11   Graph of alternating current against time

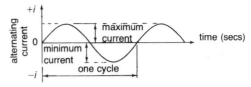

The current rises in a positive direction from zero to a maximum current, falls to zero, and then goes negative to a minimum current value and rises to zero again. This is called one cycle of the waveform.

The alternating current travels rather like the waves on the surface of a pond (see Fig 8.12).

The wave-like appearance of a graph of alternating current is why it is often called an ac waveform.

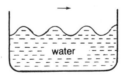

Fig 8.12   Waves on surface of water

◼ Producing an Alternating Current and Voltage

Alternating currents are produced by an oscillator. The symbol for an oscillator is shown in Fig 8.13.

A convenient method of producing alternating voltages is to use a special kind of oscillator called a **signal generator** (sometimes called an audio generator). A typical signal generator is shown in Fig 8.14.

Fig 8.13   Oscillator symbol

A signal generator will produce a regularly changing or alternating voltage.

93

Fig 8.14   Signal or audio generator

The voltage at the terminals of the signal generator changes from zero to a maximum positive value, back to zero, then to maximum negative value, and back to zero. It is the alternating voltage that causes an alternating current to flow in a circuit.

The maximum voltage of the waveform shown in Fig 8.15 is called the peak positive voltage. The minimum voltage of the waveform is called the peak negative voltage. The height above the zero level of waveform is called the amplitude. The action of the alternating voltage rising from zero to the peak

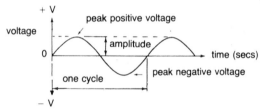

Fig 8.15   Graph of alternating voltage (ac waveform)

positive voltage, falling through zero to the peak negative voltage and returning to zero is called one cycle of the waveform. The number of cycles in a second is called the **frequency**.

You will notice that the controls of a signal generator allow the amplitude and the frequency of the waveform to be altered.

A typical alternating voltage waveform is shown in Fig 8.16.

Fig 8.16   Alternating voltage waveform

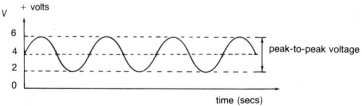

94

Alternating voltages can be superimposed on top of dc voltages. For example, the alternating voltage shown in Fig 8.16 has a maximum peak value of 6 volts and a minimum voltage of 2 volts. So the peak to peak voltage is 6−2 volts. The waveform is said to have a **peak-to-peak voltage** of 4 volts.

The alternating voltage is superimposed on a 4 volt direct voltage. The waveform never goes negative, it is always in the positive region of the graph. The voltage produced by a microphone or radio tuning circuit is a much more complicated waveform than that shown in Fig 8.16, but the action of an amplifier on such waveforms is identical to the action on the simpler waveform.

■ A Simple Amplifier

Fig 8.17 shows the circuit diagram of a simple one-transistor voltage amplifier. You should already be able to identify some of the components in the circuit and say why they are there.

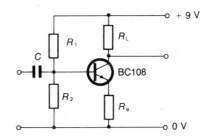

Fig 8.17   Simple one-transistor amplifier

Example
(a) What is the purpose of resistors R_1 and R_2?
   R_1 and R_2 create a potential divider to produce the correct bias for the base of the transistor.
(b) What is the purpose of resistor R_L?
   R_L is the load resistor across which the output voltage will be produced. The resistor R_e (emitter resistor) is to give the correct bias for the emitter.
(c) What effect will capacitor C have on dc?
   It will block dc. Remember a capacitor has an insulating material between the metal plates so direct current cannot flow through a capacitor.

A capacitor does however allow alternating voltages (or ac voltages) to pass through. So the purpose of C is to allow the ac signal through to the input while blocking any dc component of the signal, so that it does not affect the bias of the transistor. A capacitor used in this way is called a **coupling capacitor**.

☐ Calculation of Suitable Resistor Values

Let us assume an emitter current, I_e, of 1 mA (which is well within the maximum value for the transistor and will make our calculations easier).

   2 What will be the value of I_c?

95

We will bias our circuit to give a voltage at the collector of approximately 5 volts. This will mean that we can achieve a maximum output voltage swing of approximately 8 volts peak to peak, i.e. 4 volts above collector voltage to 4 volts below collector voltage (see Fig 8.18).

Fig 8.18 (a)   Transistor amplifier   (b)   Possible output voltage swing

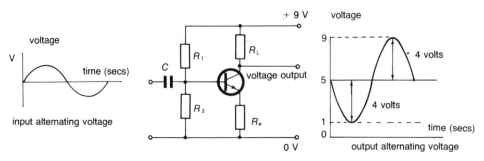

3 Why is 8 volts peak to peak the maximum output swing available?

If the output voltage is in excess of 8 volts peak to peak, it will be **clipped** at the +9 and 0 volt level (see Fig 8.19).

Fig 8.19   Clipped output voltage waveform

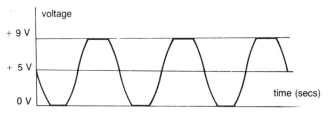

A clipped output voltage leads to **distortion** of the output signal. This should be avoided when designing an amplifier.

If the collector voltage is to be +5 volts, then the potential difference across the load resistor R_L will be 9−5 volts, i.e. 4 volts.

To calculate the value of the load resistor R_L we will use Ohm's Law:

$$R_L = \frac{V}{I} = \frac{4 \text{ volts}}{1 \text{ mA}} = \frac{4}{0.001} = 4000 \ \Omega = 4 \text{ k}\Omega$$

Hence a preferred value of 3.9 kΩ will be suitable.

Fig 8.20   Transistor amplifier – voltage across emitter resistor R_e

Suppose we design our amplifier circuit to give a voltage at the emitter of the transistor of 1 volt (see Fig 8.20).

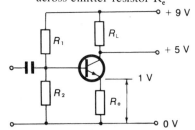

To calculate the value of the emitter resistor R_e, we will use Ohm's Law again:

$$R_e = \frac{V}{I} = \frac{1 \text{ volt}}{1 \text{ mA}} = 1000 \ \Omega = 1 \text{ k}\Omega.$$

4 What will be the voltage at the base of the transistor?

Since we are assuming a value of h_{fe} of 400 for our transistor, the base current I_b will be $\frac{1}{400}$th of the collector current I_c, i.e. $\frac{1}{400}$th of 1 mA = 0.0025 mA. The base current I_b is 0.0025 mA.

In Section 2 we described how the current in the potential divider chain, which provides the bias for the base of the transistor, is designed to be ten times the base current.

5 Can you remember the reason for this?

This means the current through the potential divider chain should be ten times the base current (I_b = 0.0025 mA). Therefore, the current through the potential divider chain is 0.025 mA.

Fig 8.21 summarises the results we have so far for the potential divider chain.

Since voltage across R_2 is 1.6 volts, voltage across R_1 must be 9−1.6 volts = 7.4 volts. As 0.025 mA flows through the chain, and 0.0025 mA flows into the base of the transistor, the current through R_1 must be 0.025 + 0.0025 = 0.0275 mA.

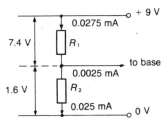

Fig 8.21   Potential divider used to bias transistor

We can now calculate the values of resistors R_1 and R_2. By Ohm's Law,

$$R = \frac{V}{I}$$

$$R_1 = \frac{7.4 \text{ volts}}{0.0275 \text{ mA}} \qquad R_2 = \frac{1.6 \text{ volts}}{0.025 \text{ mA}}$$

$$R_1 = 270 \text{ k}\Omega \qquad R_2 = 64 \text{ k}\Omega$$

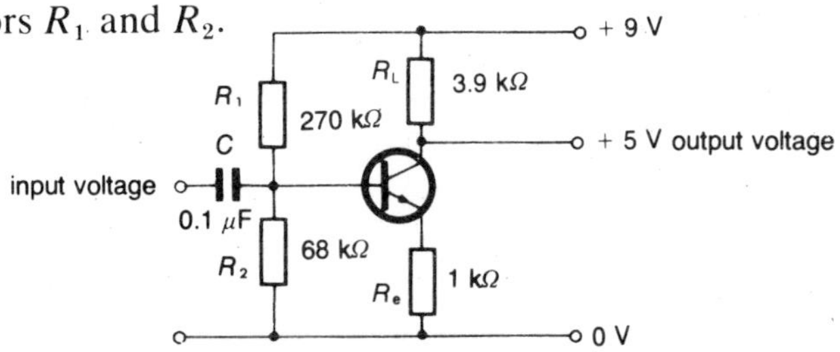

Fig 8.22   Component values for single-stage transistor amplifier

Suitable preferred values for these are therefore 270 kΩ and 68 kΩ. Finally, the value of C is not critical and a value of 0.1 μF is suitable. Activity 8, Assignment 1 in your workbook covers the building of this simple amplifier and how to check dc levels using a voltmeter.

☐ Use of Oscilloscope to Measure Voltage Gain

Activity 8, Assignment 2 deals in detail with the use of an **oscilloscope** and signal generator to measure voltage gain of your simple amplifier.

The advantage of using an oscilloscope is that it can measure peak-to-peak voltages very easily (see Fig 8.23).

$$\text{Voltage gain} = \frac{\text{change in output voltage}}{\text{change in input voltage}}$$

$$= \frac{\Delta V_o}{\Delta V_{in}}$$

and this can be measured as indicated in the assignment.

Fig 8.23   Oscilloscope

Answers to Questions

1 Audio amplifiers such as stereo amplifiers, record player amplifiers and public address amplifiers.

2 Approximately 1 mA.

3 Maximum dc voltage of the circuit is +9 V (supply voltage). The collector voltage is 5 volts, so the maximum positive swing is 4 volts.

4 1.6 volts (i.e. 1 volt + 0.6 volts 'turn-on' voltage for the transistor.

5 So that when extra current flows through resistor R_1, it does not affect the bias of the base of the transistor.

9 Amplifier Applications

◼ Design Problem: An Intercom System

We are going to design a simple intercom system that will enable sound to be transmitted by means of wires over distances up to 30 metres. The system could be used as a baby alarm, so that a baby in a bedroom can be heard in the living-room when he or she cries. An intercom could be used to communicate between the house and the garage or workshop. An **intercom system** is an electronic system that enables two people to communicate when they are separated by a distance.

One of the basic needs of human beings is to communicate with each other. Since technology is concerned with improving the quality of human life and solving problems resulting from human needs, the technology of communications is a major industry. Electronics has an important role to play in the communication industries. If human speech can be transformed into electrical signals, these can be transmitted over great distances, and then the electrical signals can be transformed back into sound for human ears. Electronics enables us to communicate information in the form of electrical signals.

1 Name another electronic or electrical system used for communicating.

◼ Intercom Systems

We are concerned with communicating human speech between two points which are fairly close together. The two points will be linked by wires which will carry electrical signals. The problem is shown in a block diagram form in Fig 9.1.

The human voice produces sound waves, which are the input of the intercom system. Speech is a form of sound energy. The intercom system converts the sound energy into electrical energy, and transmits the energy through the wires. The electrical energy must be converted back into sound energy for human ears to pick up the sound waves (the output).

Fig 9.1   Block diagram of simple communication problem

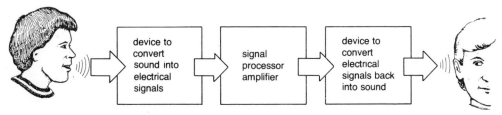

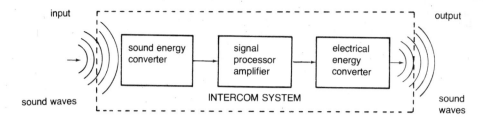

Fig 9.2   Intercom system

A device for converting sound energy into electrical energy is called a **microphone**. The circuit diagram symbol for a microphone is shown in Fig 9.3*a*. A device for converting electrical energy into sound energy is called a **loudspeaker**. The circuit diagram symbol for a loudspeaker is shown in Fig 9.3*b*.

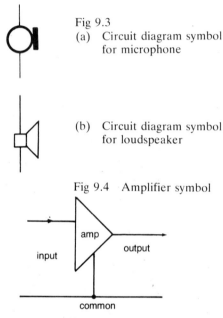

Fig 9.3
(a)   Circuit diagram symbol for microphone

(b)   Circuit diagram symbol for loudspeaker

Fig 9.4   Amplifier symbol

The electrical signals produced from a microphone are too weak to operate a loudspeaker. Therefore the signals have to be processed. The signal strength is increased by the use of an amplifier. The graphical symbol used to represent an amplifier is shown in Fig 9.4.

The **intercom** consists of a microphone, amplifier and loudspeaker. A symbolic diagram of an intercom is shown in Fig 9.5.

Fig 9.5   Symbolic diagram of intercom

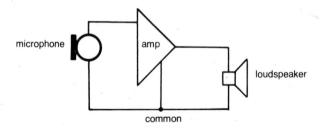

2 *What is the input to the intercom system?*
3 *What is the output of the intercom system?*
4 *Where does the amplifier obtain its power?*

■ The Crystal Microphone

The function of any microphone is to convert sound energy into electrical energy. The appearance and structure·of a **crystal microphone** are shown in Fig 9.6.

Fig 9.6   Structure of crystal microphone

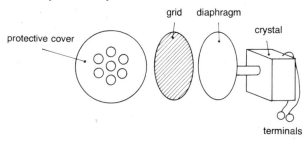

The working parts of the crystal microphone are enclosed in a thin metal case (see Fig 9.7*a*). The front cover has a regular pattern of holes to allow the entry of sound waves.

The vibrations of the air, caused by the sound waves, are transmitted through the grid to the diaphragm of the microphone. This causes the diaphragm to vibrate and stress the crystal. These stresses cause a varying potential difference across the crystal. The size of this potential difference depends upon the deflection of the crystal.

The production of a small potential difference by the mechanical deflec-

Fig 9.7 (a)   Crystal microphone   (b)   Moving coil loudspeaker

tion of a crystal is called the **piezo-electric effect**. The crystals are usually made from quartz, or Seignette salt or Rochelle salt.

■ The Moving-coil Loudspeaker

The purpose of the loudspeaker in the intercom system is to convert the amplified signals back into sound waves. The input to the loudspeaker is electrical signals and the output is sound waves.
The loudspeaker shown in Fig 9.8 contains a permanent magnet with

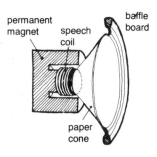

Fig 9.8   Structure of moving coil loudspeaker

cylindrical pole pieces. The speech coil is wound around a former so that it can be placed in the magnetic field. A large paper cone is rigidly attached to the former and loosely connected to a circular board which surrounds the cone and is known as a baffle board. The potential difference developed across the crystal microphone is amplified. The amplified potential difference across the loudspeaker coil produces a magnetic effect which causes the coil to be rapidly repelled and attracted by the permanent magnet. Since the coil is attached to a cone, the cone also moves backwards and forwards. This cone movement causes small, rapid changes in the pressure of the surrounding air. Our ears detect the pressure changes and we appreciate them as sounds. This type of loudspeaker is called a **moving-coil loudspeaker**. It is worthwhile remembering that a moving-coil loudspeaker can be used 'in reverse' as a microphone. Sound waves acting on the cone cause the coil to move in the magnetic field and currents are produced. (A cheap telephone earpiece can be used in electronic projects as either a microphone or a loudspeaker.)

    5 Name some everyday electronic devices that use loudspeakers.

■ The Single-stage Amplifier (Revision Section)

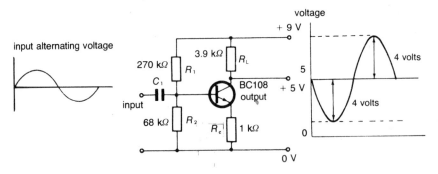

Fig 9.9   Single transistor amplifier

The purpose of the single transistor amplifier is to amplify a small input alternating voltage. The result is an amplified output which consists of a magnified alternating voltage. You may have noticed from Fig 9.9 that the input and output alternating voltages are also inverted (turned upside down). This is called signal inversion.

    6 What is the purpose of resistor R_L?
    7 What is the purpose of the capacitor C_1?
    8 What is the purpose of the resistors R_1 and R_2?

◼ The Intercom Amplifier

The first thing that you will notice about the amplifier we are going to use in the intercom is that it appears to be much more complicated than the simple amplifier of Section 8. The main reason for this is that we will need to amplify the signals from the microphone considerably in order to get a reasonably loud sound out of the loudspeaker. The amplifier shown in Fig 9.10 is called a **3-stage amplifier** because the amplification process takes place in three stages due to the three transistors T_1, T_2 and T_3. The amplified output from the first transistor is passed to the second transistor and so on.

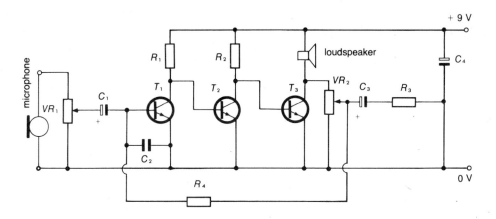

Fig 9.10   Intercom audio amplifer

Let us have a closer look at the components of the amplifier. You should already know the reasons for including many of them.

The resistors R_1 and R_2 are the load resistors for the transistors T_1 and T_2. The loudspeaker itself acts as the load for transistor T_3.

The variable resistor VR_1 acts as a potential divider so that a proportion of the output of the microphone can be fed to the amplifier. This is for **matching** purposes and will also act as a volume control.

Capacitors C_1 and C_2 are coupling capacitors.

9 Can you remember the reasons for using coupling capacitors?

Capacitor C_4 is a **smoothing capacitor** to make certain that the power supplied to the circuit has no ripple component (it is smooth). C_4 is not really necessary if a 9 V battery is used but may be necessary if the circuit is connected to a low voltage power supply.

The variable resistor VR_2, capacitor C_3 and resistors R_3 and R_4 provide a **feedback network** which helps to improve the operation of the amplifier. You do not need to know the full reason for applying feedback, but feedback in general is described in the next section.

Fig 9.11   Intercom audio amplifier (no microphone included)

■ The Effects of Feedback in Circuits

Feedback means 'feeding back' part of the output signal to the input of a circuit. This has the effect of controlling the amplification.

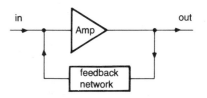

Fig 9.12   Principle of feedback

If the feedback results in an increase in the input signal, it is called **positive feedback**. Conversely, if the input signal is decreased, which results in a smaller output signal, this is called **negative feedback**.

Positive feedback tends to make the amplifier unstable and causes oscillations. The howl that is sometimes produced in a hall by a public address system is an example of positive feedback. You may notice the effect of positive feedback when you build your intercom circuit. While negative feedback has the effect of reducing the amplifier output, it is used because it has the following benefits:

(a) very stable operation of the amplifier;

(b) low distortion;

(c) reduction of noise.

In our amplifier circuit, negative feedback also helps to provide the correct bias for the base of transistor T_1.

Amplification of ac Signals

Here we will deal in more detail with the process of **amplification** by a single transistor.

Fig 9.13   DC voltage amplification

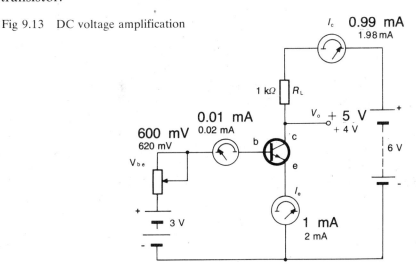

Fig 9.13 shows the typical dc conditions for a single-stage amplifier. The large and small figures represent two different sets of conditions.

The first set of conditions shows that an input voltage V_{be} of 600 mV (0.6 V 'turn-on' voltage) gives rise to a base current (I_b) of 0.01 mA. Since the current gain (h_{fe}) for a transistor is given by I_c/I_b, the gain of this transistor is 99. The collector current flowing through the load resistor R_L will give a voltage drop across R_L. By Ohm's Law this is:

$$V = I_c \times R_L = 0.99 \text{ mA} \times 1000 \text{ } \Omega = 0.99 \text{ volts} \simeq 1 \text{ volt.}$$

This means that the potential of the collector with respect to the ground rail will be $6-1$ V $= 5$ V.

If you repeat this process for the second set of conditions (small figures), you should be able to show that the potential of the collector will fall to 4 V.

By adjusting the variable resistor, the voltage across the base/emitter junction (V_{be}) is increased from 600 mV to 620 mV. Consequently, a larger base current of 0.02 mA flows into the transistor. The transistor amplifies this current and causes the collector current to increase to 1.98 mA (see Fig 9.13). This increased current flows through the load resistor R_L and produces a voltage drop across this which can be calculated by applying Ohm's Law:

$$V = I_c \times R_L = 1.98 \text{ mA} \times 1000 \text{ } \Omega = 1.98 \text{ volts} \simeq 2 \text{ volts.}$$

This means that the potential of the collector with respect to the ground rail will be 6 V$-$ 2 V $=$ 4 V. From this, it can be seen that increasing the input voltage (V_{in}) produces a decrease in the output voltage (V_{out}) from +5 volts to +4 volts. The reverse is also true, i.e. a decrease in input voltage gives a rise in the output voltage. This is known as signal inversion of the input signal and is illustrated in more detail in Fig 9.14.

105

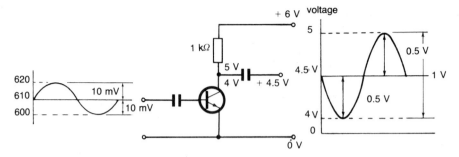

Fig 9.14   AC signal amplification

The voltage amplification of the circuit is given by:

$$\text{voltage amplification} = \frac{\text{change in output voltage}}{\text{change in input voltage}} = \frac{1\ \text{V}}{20\ \text{mV}} = 50.$$

Fig 9.14 shows an ac input signal of magnitude 20 mV peak to peak super-imposed on a base voltage of 610 mV, i.e. causing the base voltage to fluctuate between 600 and 620 mV. These figures correspond to those discussed in Fig 9.13 and give rise to the output voltage shown in Fig 9.14, i.e. 1 V peak to peak. The input and output wave diagrams also show the inversion of the signal.

In practice, the transistor must be biased, and this is achieved by the use of two resistors as a potential divider. The static dc conditions of transistor amplification produce steady currents for the base, emitter and collector (see Fig 9.15). The dynamic working of the transistor results in the amplification of alternating signals and signal inversion (see Fig 9.15).

Fig 9.15   Operating conditions for single transistor amplifier

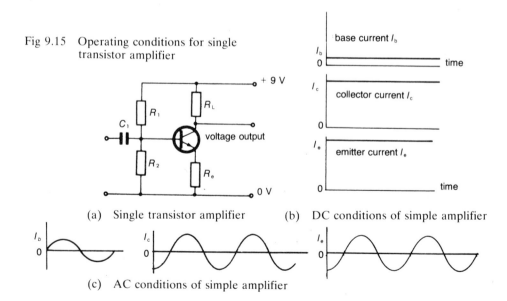

(a)   Single transistor amplifier

(b)   DC conditions of simple amplifier

(c)   AC conditions of simple amplifier

106

Answers to Questions

1 Telephone system, radio or television.
2 Sound waves, perhaps speech.
3 Sound waves from the loudspeaker for the human ear.
4 From an external power source, such as a battery or a dc power supply.
5 Stereo amplifiers and record players, transistor radios, televisions, public address systems in railway stations, airport terminals and at sporting activities.
6 Resistor R_L is called the load resistor: it is necessary to provide an output voltage.
7 It blocks any dc from the input signal source, but allows an ac signal to pass.
8 They provide the potential divider network of resistors to bias the transistor.
9 To allow ac signals through. To block any dc which would affect the biasing of the transistor.

10 Radio Circuits

■ Introduction

We are now going to study simple radio systems and explain the purpose of the components in a radio. Your practical work will be to build and test a simple tuner that can be coupled to the amplifier that you built in Section 9.

Why do we need radio?

Sound waves will not travel very great distances and to use a system similar to the intercom that you built in Section 9 would be very inconvenient and costly. Imagine running wires from Broadcasting House to every home in the country!

Radio broadcasting means converting the sound waves into radio waves which can then be transmitted long distances through the air or space. We tend to take radio very much for granted these days, but if you think for a little while about some of the numerous applications of radio communication, you will realise how important it is for our lives today. A list of these applications might include the following:

(a) radio and television;
(b) aircraft and satellite communications;
(c) police and ambulance call services;
(d) radio control of models.

You may be able to think of other applications.

■ Essential Components of a Radio System

We have already seen how sound waves can be converted into electrical energy.

1 Name a device for converting sound energy into electrical energy.

Fig 10.1 Radio communication system

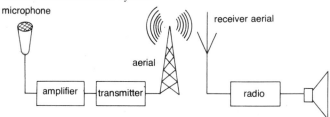

Fig 10.1 shows, in a simple block diagram form, the essential parts of a radio communication system. The electrical signals from the microphone are amp-

lified and converted into radio waves by the **transmitter**. These are then radiated out (broadcast) by the **transmitting aerial**. In order to detect these radio waves, a receiving aerial is needed and this is connected to the radio. The radio waves received by the aerial are weak and require amplification. The radio receiver usually contains an amplifier circuit to operate the loud-speaker.

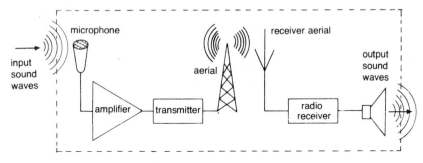

Fig 10.2 Radio system (input and output)

The input to the radio system is sound waves into the microphone. The sound could be human speech or music or a mixture of different sounds. The output from the loudspeaker of the radio is also sound waves which are received by the human ear.

■ Sound Waves

Sound waves travel in air but sound will not travel through a vacuum. Air consists of tiny particles or molecules. Sound waves compress the air by a very small amount. When compressed, the particles move closer together but the natural springiness of the air tends to separate them. This elastic property allows sound to travel through air in waves (see Fig 10.3).

Fig 10.3 (a) Sound travelling as pressure waves in air-filled tube

(b) Sound travelling as pressure waves in air

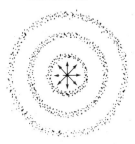

Sound moves through air without permanent displacement of the air particles. The sound causes layers of air particles to vibrate. Waves travel on water in a similar way, except the water particles move up and down (see Fig 10.4).

Fig 10.4 Water particles move up and down as wave travels in water

direction of wave movement

waves on surface of water

water

Human vocal chords can produce very complicated sound waves (see Fig 10.5). The human ear is very sensitive to vibrations in the air resulting from travelling sound waves.

Fig 10.5　Human sound production and reception

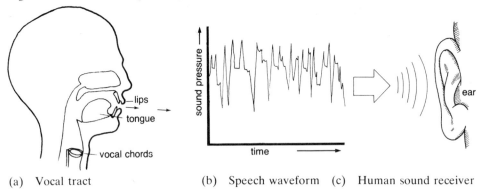

(a)　Vocal tract　　　　(b)　Speech waveform　(c)　Human sound receiver

Human speech is a complex waveform when displayed on an oscilloscope. You could connect a crystal microphone to an oscilloscope and produce a trace as shown in Fig 10.6

Fig 10.6　Speech through microphone displayed on oscilloscope

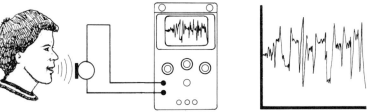

Playing a musical instrument close to a microphone and displaying the waveform on an oscilloscope, produces a more regular waveform (see Fig 10.7).

Tuning forks are often used by musician· to tune their instruments. When a tuning fork is gently struck in front of a microphone, the

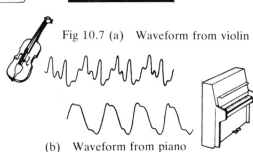

Fig 10.7 (a)　Waveform from violin

(b)　Waveform from piano

waveform displayed on an oscilloscope is smooth and regular. This waveform is called a sine wave (see Fig 10.8). It is similar to the alternating current waveform.

Fig 10.8　Sine wave (similar to ac waveform)

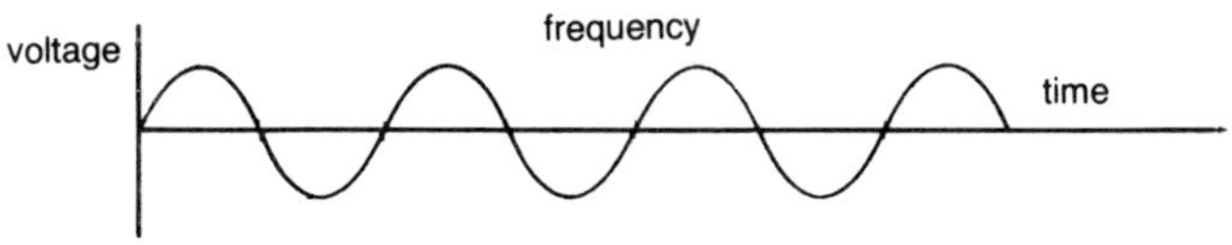

110

■ Radio Waves

Radio waves are a group of waves that are part of a very much larger series or spectrum of waves. These are called **electromagnetic waves** because they consist of a mixture of an electric and a magnetic wave. Electromagnetic waves may be distinguished by their **frequency** or number of wave cycles per second (see Fig 10.9).

Fig 10.10 shows the complete electromagnetic spectrum with the frequencies along the left-hand side of the diagram.
The unit of measurement of frequency is the **Hertz (Hz)**. 1 wave or 1 cycle per second is 1 Hertz (1 Hz). Radio waves have frequencies between 10 kHz and 1000 MHz (i.e. between 10 000 Hz and 1 000 000 000 Hz).

Radio waves are also classified according to their position in the spectrum of radio frequencies, as shown in Fig 10.11. You will notice that different parts of the range are used for different types of transmission. We will be particularly concerned with the waves at the lower end of the range (i.e. radio broadcasts 100 kHz to 1 MHz).

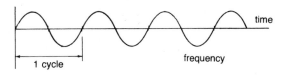

Fig 10.9   Waveform (frequency)

Fig 10.10   Electromagnetic spectrum

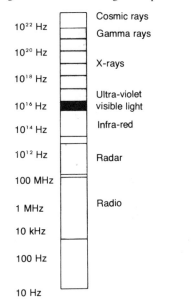

Fig 10.11   Radio frequencies

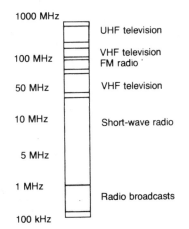

■ Radio Wavelengths

You may be more familiar with the **wavelength** of radio broadcasts than the frequency.

Radio 4 broadcasts on 1500 metres wavelength.

Fig 10.12 shows that wavelength is a measurement of distance. The wavelength of a wave is measured in metres (m). The wavelength (λ) of a wave and its frequency (f) are related by the equation $v = f\lambda$, where v is the velocity of the wave.

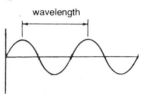

Fig 10.12   Wavelength

The velocity of all electromagnetic waves is the same in air, i.e. 3×10^8 m/s (300 000 000 m/s).

What is the frequency of Radio 4?

$v = f \times \lambda$

$3 \times 10^8 = f \times 1500$

$\therefore f = 2 \times 10^5$ or 200 000 Hz.

The frequency of Radio 4 is 200 kHz.

Programme	Wavelength (metres)	Frequency (kHz)
Radio 1	285 and 275	1053 and 1089
Radio 2	433 and 330	693 and 909
Radio 3	247	1215
Radio 4	1500	200

■ Modulated Waveforms

You may by now have realised that the frequencies that we have been talking about are higher than the human ear can hear. The highest frequency that we can hear clearly is about 20 kHz. How then are we able to hear radio broadcasts?

In order to answer this question, we must first explain a little more about radio waves. If the sound from a microphone, say of frequency 1000 Hz, was transmitted, this wave would carry only a very short distance through the air. Waves of much higher frequency do however travel much greater distances through the air. The problem of transmitting the lower frequency signals is overcome in a very ingenious way. A wave of high frequency is used to carry the wave of low frequency. This high frequency wave is called a **carrier wave**. The radio frequencies shown in Fig 10.11 are the carrier wave frequencies.

If the carrier wave were transmitted on its own, nothing would be heard when it was picked up by the radio receiver. In order for the carrier wave to carry information, it must be modified or **modulated** in some way. One way in which this can be done is by varying the carrier amplitude at the frequency of the sound signals that are to be transmitted.

The frequency of the sound waves to be transmitted by radio waves is often called the **audio frequency (AF)**.

Fig 10.13 shows how the audio frequency (AF) signal is used to vary the amplitude of the carrier wave or **radio frequency (RF)** wave.

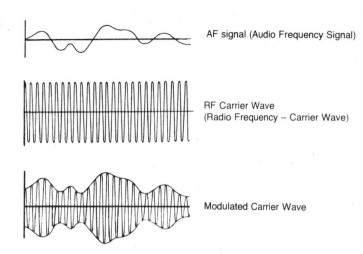

AF signal (Audio Frequency Signal)

RF Carrier Wave
(Radio Frequency – Carrier Wave)

Modulated Carrier Wave

Fig 10.13   Principle of modulation of carrier waves

■ More Detailed Layout of Radio System

The detailed layout of a radio system is shown in Fig 10.14. Radio frequency waves or carrier waves are produced at the broadcasting station by a radio frequency oscillator (RF oscillator). The sound waves are converted into electrical signals by a microphone. These signals are amplified in the broadcasting station. The audio frequency waves are mixed with the radio frequency waves in a modulator. The modulated carrier wave is transmitted from a transmitter aerial in the broadcasting station. These modulated radio waves can be picked up by numerous radio receivers.

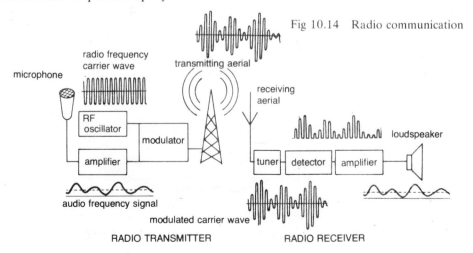

Fig 10.14   Radio communication

113

The Functions of a Radio Receiver

The radio receiver must do three things:
- (a) It must be able to separate one broadcasting station from another. This is called **tuning** in to the station.
- (b) It must be able to separate the audio frequencies from the radio frequency in the modulated wave. This is called **demodulating** or detecting.
- (c) It must amplify the audio frequencies.

We have already studied the structure of the amplifier so we shall look in some detail at the design of tuning and demodulating circuits.

Tuning Circuits

A simple **tuning circuit** consists of a capacitor connected in parallel with a **coil** of wire. The coil is often wound on a **ferrite rod** as ferrite is a magnetic material that increases the magnetic effect of the coil.

In Section 6, you learned that a capacitor connected to a resistor will discharge at a rate that depends upon the size of the capacitor and the resistor. The coil in a tuning circuit, such as that shown in Fig 10.15, is an 'active' component like

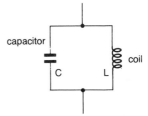

Fig 10.15   Simple tuning circuit

the capacitor. The coil can also store charge. In a tuning circuit, if the capacitor is charged and then allowed to discharge through the coil, the charge is transferred to the coil. The coil then discharges and the charge returns to the capacitor. The rate at which this charge/discharge process takes place depends upon the size of the capacitor and the coil. The resulting current in the circuit oscillates, and the waves produced are the same as the ac waveforms that we have come across before. If the capacitor is a variable capacitor, the rate at which the circuit oscillates can be varied.

When a tuning circuit is used to detect a radio signal, the frequency of oscillation of the tuning circuit is adjusted to be the same as the frequency of the radio frequency (RF) transmission. The effect of this is to give a build-up in the size of the oscillations in the tuning circuit. The circuit is said to be 'tuned in'.

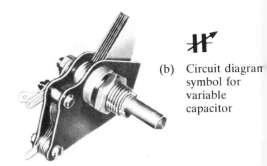

(b) Circuit diagram symbol for variable capacitor

Fig 10.16 (a)   Variable capacitor

■ An Improved Tuning Circuit

In practice, the simple circuit described above would not be very selective. This means that it would not easily be able to separate the signals from different stations. A more **selective tuning circuit** can be made as shown in Fig 10.17.

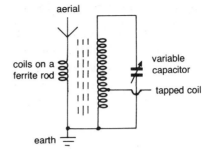

Fig 10.17 Selective tuning circuit diagram

Two coils are wound on the same ferrite rod and the signal is taken from a connection or tapping on the larger coil as indicated. This is the circuit that you will be constructing for your activity work.

■ Demodulation

2 What is meant by demodulation?

The average value of the modulated signal as shown in Fig 10.18 is zero. This is because there are as many negative parts to the wave as there are positive parts. This would produce no sound from the radio loudspeaker.

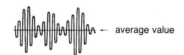

Fig 10.18 Average value of modulated signal

In order to demodulate the signal it is passed through a diode. A **diode** is a semiconductor device which will only allow a current to flow through it in one direction.

The direction of flow of conventional current through a diode is indicated by the arrow of the circuit diagram symbol (see Fig 10.19).

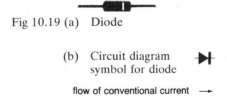

Fig 10.19 (a)   Diode

(b)   Circuit diagram symbol for diode

flow of conventional current ⟶

A diode will only allow the positive or forward parts of the modulated signal to pass through it and the result is as shown in Fig 10.20.

Fig 10.20   Demodulated signal

The average value of this demodulated signal is also shown. Notice that the fluctuations of the average value of the demodulated signal follow the original fluctuations of the audio frequency (AF).

115

When the amplified average value of the demodulated signal is fed into a loudspeaker, a faithful reproduction of the original sound is produced. The final tuning circuit is shown in Fig 10.21. When this tuning circuit is coupled to your amplifier, you should be able to listen to a radio broadcast.

Fig 10.21 (a) Circuit diagram of   (b) Full tuning circuit
                full tuning circuit

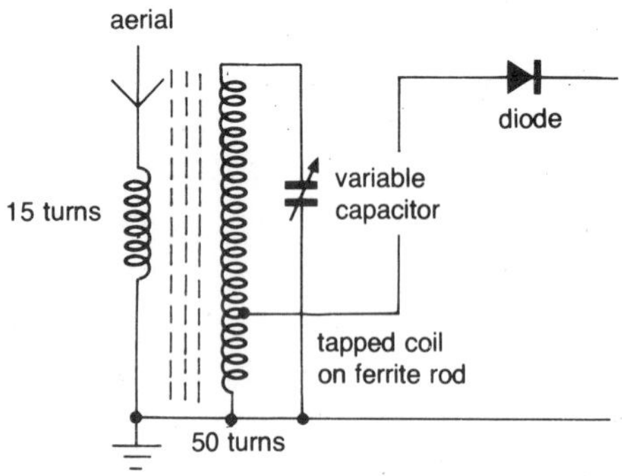

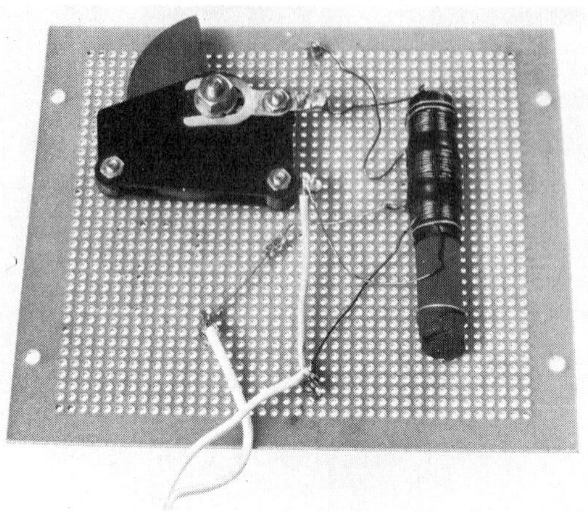

Answers to Questions
1 A microphone.
2 The separation of the audio frequency (AF) waves from the radio frequency (RF) waves in a modulated signal.

11 Power Supplies

■ Introduction

A **power supply** is an electrical device for converting the power available from the ac mains into dc power. Power supplies are used in laboratories to provide dc power for experimental electronic work.

Many everyday electronic devices that need to be run from the ac mains use semiconductor devices such as transistors and diodes. Transistor circuits require a direct current (dc) supply.

  1. What is the dc power supply used on the electronic circuits built in this module?

Constantly replacing batteries can be expensive, and it is more convenient to use the ac mains power if it can be converted into dc power. Power supplies are used to convert ac power into dc power in transistor radios, solid state televisions, record players and model railway controllers.

The particular application of a power supply that you will be concerned with building in your practical work is called a battery eliminator. A **battery eliminator** can replace the 9 V battery used to power the transistor circuits in this module

■ Components of a Power Supply

Fig 11.1 shows a block diagram of the essential components of a power supply; ac mains input can be obtained from the normal supply sockets in your laboratory or workshop.

Fig 11.1   Block diagram of power supply

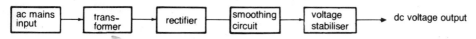

  2 What is the supply voltage of the ac mains?

The essential components of a power supply are:

  The **transformer** which enables the 240 V of the ac supply to be converted either up or down according to the size of the output required from the power supply.

  The **rectifier** which converts the ac from the transformer into dc.

117

The **smoothing circuit** which reduces fluctuations in the current or voltage after it has been rectified.

The **voltage stabilizer** which ensures that, as the current drawn from the power supply changes, the output voltage remains constant.

In this Section, these essential components will be examined in some detail.

■ Generation of Alternating Current

The electric power which we receive in our homes, factories and schools is generated at a power station. The power is produced by rotating a large coil of wire in a powerful magnetic field. In practice, the process is more complicated than this but a simple explanation is quite adequate at this stage.

When a wire is moved through a magnetic field, a current is produced in the wire. (This was mentioned in Section 9 when we talked about the use of a moving-coil loudspeaker as a microphone.) The direction of the current depends upon the direction of movement of the wire and the direction of the magnetic field. The size of the current depends upon the rate at which the wire moves through the magnetic field. It is called an **induced current**.

Fig 11.2 shows a single coil rotating in a magnetic field. At the instant shown, conductor AD is moving up and perpendicular to the magnetic field and will have a current induced in it as shown. Conductor BC is moving down and the current induced in it will be in the opposite direction. Current flows round the coil in the direction shown. We will call this the positive direction of current flow. We can represent the current flow as shown in Fig 11.3. A cross-section of the coil shows the current in AD flowing away from you and current in BC flowing towards you.

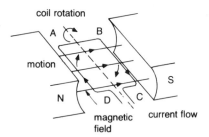

Fig 11.2   Coil in magnetic field

Fig 11.3   Cross-section of coil

Fig 11.4 shows the induced current direction as the coil continues to rotate.

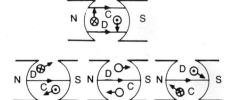

Fig 11.4   Rotation of coil

At position *a* the conductors are no longer moving perpendicular to the field and the size of the current is reduced. At position *b* the conductors are moving parallel to the field and no current is induced. At position *c* the conductors are starting to move in the opposite directions to those of Fig 11.3

and the direction of the induced current is reversed. If a graph is plotted of induced current against time (coil position), the result is as shown in Fig 11.5. H and V refer to the times when the coil is horizontal or vertical and the positions corresponding to a, b, c of Fig 11.4 are shown.

One complete rotation of the coil produces one waveform cycle. This is the alternating current (ac) waveform that we used in Section 8. One complete waveform is called one **cycle**. The number of cycles per second is called the frequency of the waveform. Frequency is measured in Hertz (Hz). 1 cycle per second equals 1 Hz.

Fig 11.5   Graph of alternating current

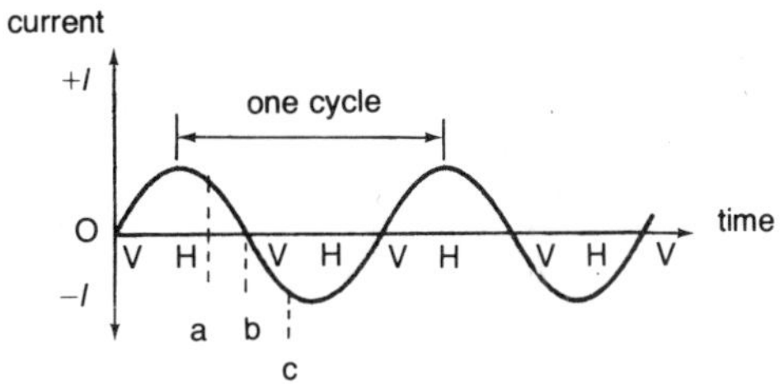

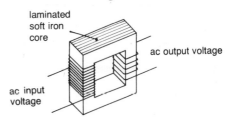

The frequency of the ac mains supply in this country is 50 Hz or 50 cycles per second.

◼ Transformers

The function of a transformer is to change the size of an ac voltage. A transformer relies on induction for its operation. In the case of the transformer, the magnetic field changes through the conductor rather than the conductor moving through the field as in the case of a generator.

A typical transformer consists of two insulated wire coils wound round a laminated soft iron core. The input coil is called the **primary coil**. The output coil is called the **secondary coil**. An alternating voltage is connected to the input of the primary coil. The required output voltage appears across the ends of the secondary coil.

If there are more wire turns on the secondary than on the primary coil, the output will be larger than the input. This is called a **step-up transformer**. If there are less wire turns on the secondary than on the primary coil, the output will be smaller than the input. This is called a **step-down transformer**.

Fig 11.6   Transformer

Fig 11.7 (a)   Step-down transformer

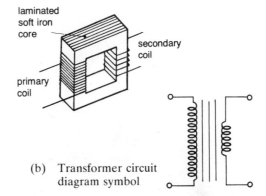

(b)   Transformer circuit diagram symbol

119

The ratio $\dfrac{\text{number of turns on secondary coil}}{\text{number of turns on primary coil}}$

is called the **turns ratio** of the transformer. This is also equal to the

voltage ratio: $\dfrac{\text{output voltage across secondary coil}}{\text{input voltage across primary coil}}$

$\therefore \dfrac{\text{output voltage across secondary coil}}{\text{input voltage across primary coil}} = \dfrac{\text{number of turns on secondary coil}}{\text{number of turns on primary coil}}$

Example

How many turns are needed on the secondary coil of a transformer which has 1000 turns on the primary, in order to step down an ac voltage from 240 V to 12 V?

Voltage ratio $= \dfrac{\text{output voltage across secondary coil}}{\text{input voltage across primary coil}} = \dfrac{12\ \text{V}}{240\ \text{V}} = \dfrac{1}{20}.$

Turns ratio $= \dfrac{\text{number of turns on secondary coil}}{\text{number of turns on primary coil}} = \dfrac{?}{1000}$

Voltage ratio = turns ratio, so $\dfrac{1}{20} = \dfrac{\text{number of turns on secondary coil}}{1000}$

$\therefore$ Number of turns on secondary coil $= \dfrac{1}{20} \times 1000 = 50.$

■ AC Mains Voltage

The domestic ac mains voltage which we receive in our homes and schools has a value of 240 volts ac. In Section 8, we described the peak-to-peak value of an alternating voltage.

Fig 11.8 shows the ac mains voltage waveform with the peak values for a 240 V ac supply. Notice that the peak-to-peak value of this is 680 V ac.

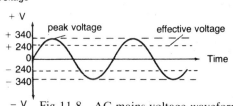

Fig 11.8   AC mains voltage waveform

Since the waveform only reaches its peak value of about 340 V for a fraction of the cycle, the **effective value** of the voltage in a circuit is less than the peak value. The effective value is 240 V. The peak voltage is about 340 V. A voltage waveform with an effective value of 240 V ac would have the same effect in a circuit as a steady 240 V dc. The effective voltage value is also called the **root mean square (rms)** value of the voltage. Alternating currents also have rms values.

■ Electrical Safety

When you come to your practical work for this section, you will be wiring a transformer to the mains supply. It is essential that you know about using mains electricity safely. Electricity can be dangerous. It can give you a serious electric shock which could be fatal. Electrical faults can also cause fires. You should always take a few simple precautions to reduce the dangers.

Always use three-pin mains sockets which are earthed (see Fig 11.9). Make absolutely certain that your plug is wired correctly. Fig 11.10 shows the correct wiring of a three-pin plug.

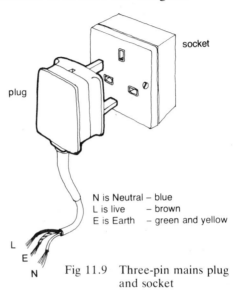

N is Neutral – blue
L is live   – brown
E is Earth   – green and yellow

Fig 11.9   Three-pin mains plug and socket

Why three pins? The **live** and **neutral** connections are the two that are necessary in order to complete the circuit; the **earth** connection ensures that if anything goes wrong with the circuit, the fuse will blow and cut off the supply. Earth means literally a connection to a metal rod which is fixed into the ground. Metal cases of domestic appliances, water pipes and the metal boxes for light and power sockets should all be earthed. If something goes wrong, causing the metal to become 'live', a large current can flow to earth and the fuse will blow.

Fig 11.10   Correct wiring of plug

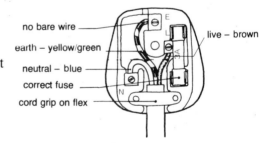

no bare wire
earth – yellow/green
neutral – blue
correct fuse
cord grip on flex
live – brown

When wiring a plug, it is essential that the wires are connected in the proper manner. Only strip off enough of the insulation on each wire to enable connections to be made. A useful way of remembering which wire goes to which terminal is that the second letter of the colour is the initial letter of the direction, i.e. bLue = Left and bRown = Right. This means that when looking from the top of the plug, the blue wire goes to the left-hand terminal and the brown wire goes to the right-hand terminal as shown in Fig 11.10. When the three wires are connected, the cable grip should be secured, making sure it grips the outer covering of the flex and not the conductor covering. Most plugs used today are of the 13 A type and contain a fuse. It is essential that the correct fuse is used – a 3 A fuse is perfectly adequate for your power supply.

121

■ Rectification: The Diode

3 What does rectification mean?

Diodes are used to convert alternating current into direct current. The **diode** is a semiconductor device rather like a transistor but with only two leads. Inside the plastic case of the diode is a small piece of silicon. The silicon consists of a junction of p-type silicon and n-type silicon. It is often called a p-n junction diode (see Fig 11.11a).

Fig 11.11 shows the appearance of a junction diode and its circuit symbol. Notice that the direction of current flow is the same as the direction of the arrow of the diode symbol (Fig 11.11b). The cathode is identified by a band round the diode body (Fig 11.11c), although a simple test in a dc circuit can always be made if the marking is not clear.

Fig 11.11 Appearance of junction diode and its circuit diagram symbol

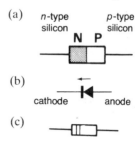

The diode is a 'one way' device. Current can only flow through it when it is forward biased. This means that current can only flow through the diode if the p-type silicon is towards the positive terminal of the battery or power supply, and the n-type silicon is towards the negative terminal (see Fig 11.12a). If the diode is reverse biased, no current (or very little current) will flow. A reverse bias diode would have the n-type silicon towards the positive terminal of the battery or power supply (see Fig 11.12b).

Fig 11.12 Circuit to demonstrate forward and reverse biasing of diode
(a) Forward biased diode   (b) Reverse biased diode

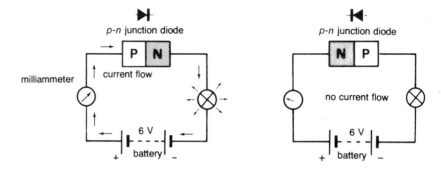

■ Rectifier Circuits

The circuit shown in Fig 11.13 will produce **half-wave rectification**. The diode will conduct for the half cycle of alternating current when it is forward biased, but will not conduct for the half cycle when the diode is reverse biased.

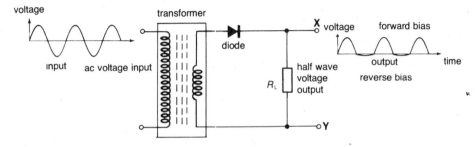

Fig 11.13   Half wave rectification

The half-wave rectified output can be seen by connecting the output across the load resistor R_L from points X and Y to an oscilloscope.

Full-wave rectification can be obtained by using a transformer with a centre-tapped secondary coil, as shown in Fig 11.14. This ensures that when one diode is forward biased the other is reverse biased and vice versa. Full-wave rectification produces the output voltage waveform shown in Fig 11.14. This is the type of rectification circuit you will be using for your battery eliminator power supply.

Fig 11.14   Full wave rectification

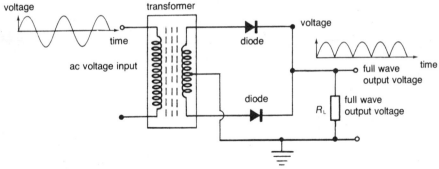

☐ Bridge Rectifier

Fig 11.15 shows an alternative full-wave rectifier circuit. Four diodes can be connected in a bridge network across the secondary coil of the transformer.

Fig 11.15   Bridge rectifier circuit

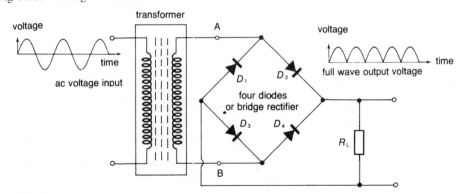

This produces full-wave rectified voltage at the output of the circuit. You should be able to satisfy yourself that the current flow is always in the same direction through R_L; i.e. when A is positive and B is negative, current flows through $D_2 - R_L - D_3$; when B is positive and A is negative, current flows through $D_4 - R_L - D_1$.

Bridge rectifiers are available with the four diodes and connections encapsulated in one container (see Fig 11.16).

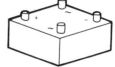

Fig 11.16   Plastic encapsulated bridge rectifier

■ Smoothing

The output from rectifier circuits is not very smooth; we say the output has a large ripple (see Fig 11.17).

Fig 11.17   Large ripple on full wave rectified output

It is necessary to produce a smoother output voltage waveform. **Smoothing** can be obtained by putting a capacitor across the output of the rectifier circuit, In Section 6, you saw that a capacitor discharges slowly through a resistor in a time period which depends upon the time constant (CR) of the circuit. If capacitor C is made fairly large, it will only have discharged a very little by the time that the next peak of the rectified output has arrived to charge it up again. The effect of smoothing is shown in Fig 11.18. The smoothing is improved with a larger time constant CR. This is usually achieved by increasing the value of the capacitor C rather than the load resistor R_L, but note that the diodes have to pass a greater current.

Fig 11.18 (a)   Full wave rectification circuit with capacitor smoothing   (b)   Smoothed output voltage

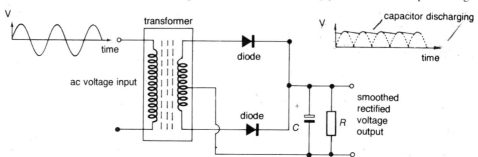

■ Voltage Stabilisation

If the reverse bias across an ordinary diode is increased, the diode will eventually **break down** and be ruined. There are, however, special diodes called **Zener diodes** that are designed to break down.

124

A characteristic graph of voltage against current flow through a Zener diode is shown in Fig 11.19. When the Zener diode is reverse biased, a breakdown will occur at one particular voltage (say 9.1 volts), and the characteristic of one such diode is shown.

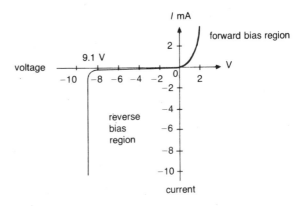

Fig 11.19   Zener diode characteristics

Notice that once the breakdown has occurred, the voltage across the diode remains constant for a large range of currents. This constant voltage can be used for reference purposes in a stabilisation circuit. The outward appearance of a Zener diode is very similar to an ordinary diode. They are manufactured in a range of **reference voltages**. A Zener diode should always be used with a series resistor to make sure that the power dissipated by it is within its designed limits.

In practice, while a Zener diode used as in Fig 11.21 will provide a stable ouput voltage, the circuit does have undesirable limitations.

Fig 11.20   Zener diode circuit symbol

One way to overcome these is to use the diode to hold the base of a transistor at a fixed voltage, so that there is a voltage greater than the 'turn on' voltage (0.6 volts) across the emitter/base junction. The transistor can then be used to handle the power required from the circuit.

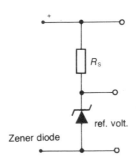

Fig 11.21   Use of series resistor with Zener diode

In the circuit shown in Fig 11.22, the Zener diode D holds the base of transistor T at a constant voltage (the reference voltage). This enables the transistor to control the power output.

Fig 11.22   Transistorised voltage stabiliser

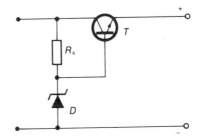

■ Stabilised Power Supply

Fig 11.23 shows the final version of the stabilised power supply you are going to build. Before you start on the circuit, it would be a good idea to go over the circuit and try to explain the reason for using each component.

Fig 11.23   Stabilised power supply (battery eliminator)

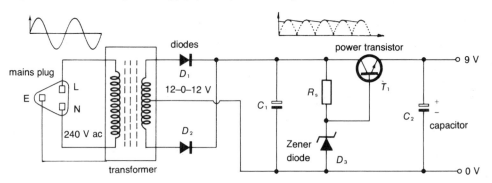

Answers to Questions

1   A battery.
2   240 volts ac.
3   Converting ac into dc.

12 Operational Amplifiers

■ Integrated Circuits

In previous Sections, the circuits described were made up from discrete electronic components. That is, individual electronic components, like transistors, diodes, resistors and capacitors, were used to make switching circuits, power supplies and amplifiers. Transistor electronics was developed during the 1950's. Between the two World Wars, electronic equipment for radio broadcasting and navigation used thermionic valves. The introduction of transistors meant that electronic equipment, like radios, could be made much smaller. In the early 1960's, the 'integrated electronic circuit' was introduced. An **integrated circuit** is a tiny chip of semiconducting material, usually silicon, where a whole electronic circuit is produced on the chip. The silicon chip, about 0.2 mm square, is encased in a plastic or ceramic case with connecting leads (see Fig 12.1).

Fig 12.1 Magnified section of integrated circuit with part of case removed to show silicon chip

The four basic electronic components – transistors, diodes, resistors and capacitors – can all be formed on the tiny silicon chip.

Conventional wire connections between these components are not necessary. Combinations of the four electronic components can make an entire circuit in a compact package. For example, complete audio amplifier circuits can be produced in a single integrated circuit (see Fig 12.2).

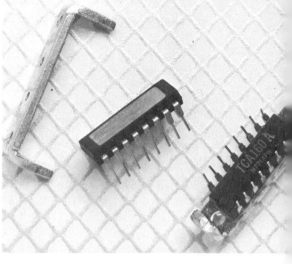

Fig 12.2   Integrated circuits used in audio amplifiers

Some integrated circuits contain **digital circuits**. Digital circuits process information in the form of digits or numbers. Electrical signals are used to represent information in a digital form. An electronic circuit can be in one of two states, either conducting or not conducting. For example, a switch can be 'on' or 'off'. Many logical processes can be broken down into simple questions requiring an answer 'yes' or 'no'. The information can be represented by the binary digits 1 and 0 (e.g. 'yes' represented by 1 and 'no' represented by 0, or 'on' represented by 1 and 'off' represented by 0). Digital circuits use electrical voltages to represent the binary states 1 and 0.

Many integrated circuits are digital circuits; they contain logic gates or counting circuits. A complete counting circuit may be contained in the integrated circuit package (see Figs 12.3 and 12.4).

Fig 12.3   Tiny integrated circuit is a decade counter containing over 120 components

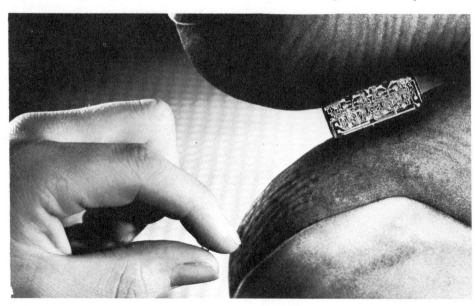

The computer industry is one of the major users of digital integrated circuits. A computer may contain many digital integrated circuits mounted on printed circuit boards (see Fig 12.5). Miniaturisation of electronic components has meant that modern computers may contain hundreds of complete digital circuits. The printed circuit boards are assembled in panels which make up the central processor of the computer (see Fig 12.6).

Adding machines, pocket calculators and computers all use digital integrated circuits. The growing demand for these electronic devices in recent years has resulted in miniaturised circuits, reliable components and a reduction in the cost of integrated circuits.

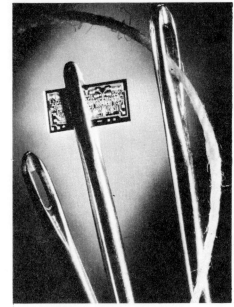

Fig 12.4   Relative size of silicon chip in integrated circuit compared with needle

Fig 12.5   Digital integrated circuits mounted on printed circuit board of modern computer

Fig 12.6 Digital integrated circuit boards assembled in central processor of computer

Fig 12.7 ICL 2904 Computer

■ Operational Amplifiers

The integrated circuit operational amplifier was developed, as its name suggests, to perform mathematical operations. When the 'op amp' is connected in a circuit with appropriate components, it will perform mathematical operations on electrical voltages. The **operational amplifier** can be used to add, subtract, multiply, divide, differentiate and integrate electrical voltages. It is often used for analogue computing, and also for instrumentation and control applications.

In this Section, the operational amplifier will be used mainly as a differential amplifier. We will use an integrated circuit form of the operational amplifier called the 741 Op Amp (see Fig 12.8).

The 741 Op Amp can be obtained in a round can, rather like a transistor, or in a rectangular plastic package with 8 pins or 14 pins. We shall use the dual-in-line

Fig 12.8   741 Operational Amplifier

(DIL) package with 8 leads (see Fig 12.8). This 741 Op Amp is called an **8-pin dual-in-line** package. The distance between each of the leads or pins down either side of the 741 Op Amp is 0.1″. This makes it easy to solder the Op Amp on to 0.1″ matrix copper stripboard.

■ The 741 Operational Amplifier

Inside the plastic package of a 741 Op Amp is a small silicon chip containing a complete linear amplifier circuit. This complex circuit contains about twenty transistors, eleven resistors and a capacitor. It is not necessary to know what the circuit looks like, only what functions the 741 Op Amp can perform. We can treat the Op Amp as a **black box** amplifier. The amplifier symbol is drawn as a triangle (see Fig 12.9). The black box amplifier has input terminals and an output terminal. The amplifier will perform the operation of amplifying the input signals. The

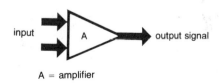

A = amplifier

Fig 12.9   Black box amplifier

Fig 12.10   Amplifier inputs and output

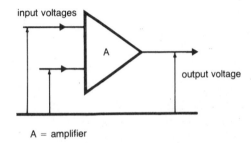

A = amplifier

131

input signals going into the operational amplifier are **input voltages** and the output signal is an **output voltage**. The operational amplifier performs an amplification operation on the difference between the two input voltages. It is for this reason that the amplifier is sometimes called a 'differential amplifier'.

The 741 Op Amp has two input terminals, an inverting input and a non-inverting input (see Fig 12.11). The inverting input terminal is identified by a minus sign and the non-inverting input terminal is identified by a plus sign. The 741 Op Amp has one output terminal. The operational amplifier needs a power supply. It has one terminal connected to the positive polarity of the supply and one terminal connected to the negative polarity of the supply (see Fig 12.11).

The pin connection of the 741 Op Amp can be determined from a diagram of the top view of the dual-in-line package, as shown in Fig 12.13. The actual plastic package of the 8-pin dual-in-line 741 Op Amp has a small circular indentation or dot on the top surface – this indicates pin 1. The pins are determined by numbering from 1 to 8 in an anticlockwise direction (see Figs 12.12 and 12.13).

The supply voltage should not exceed +18 volts on the positive supply and −18 volts on the negative supply.

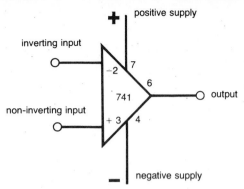

Fig 12.11   741 Op Amp circuit diagram symbol

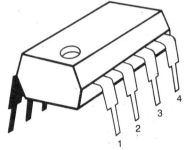

Fig 12.12   Eight-pin dual-in-line 741 Op Amp

Fig 12.13   Pin connections for eight-pin DIL 741 Op Amp

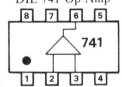

Pin 1	Offset null.	No need to make connection to this terminal in the circuits in this module. Sometimes a variable resistor is connected between pins 1 and 5 in order to zero (or nullify) the output when the input is zero.
Pin 2	Inverting input.	
Pin 3	Non-inverting input.	
Pin 4	Connection to negative of power supply.	
Pin 5	Offset null.	
Pin 6	Output.	
Pin 7	Connection to positive of power supply.	
Pin 8	No connection.	

Using the 741 Op Amp as a Linear Amplifier

Amplifiers are used to convert small voltage changes at the input into larger voltage changes at the output. The amplifying property is measured by the **voltage gain** of the amplifier. The amplifier voltage gain A_V is the change in output voltage divided by the change in input voltage,

$$\text{i.e. voltage gain } A_V = \frac{\text{change in output voltage}}{\text{change in input voltage}}.$$

Example
If the change in input voltage to an amplifier is 10 millivolts and the change in output voltage is 1 volt, what is the voltage gain of the amplifier?

$$\text{Voltage gain } A_V = \frac{1\text{ V}}{10\text{ mV}} = \frac{1\text{ V}}{0.01\text{ V}} \quad \therefore A_V = 100$$

The voltage gain is 100.

When the change in output voltage is directly proportional to the change in input voltage, the amplifier functions in a linear way. Such an amplifier is called a **linear amplifier**. Electronic engineers usually try to design linear amplifiers, although most amplifiers have some non-linearity.

The 741 Op Amp performs in almost a linear way, as shown by the graph in Fig 12.14. In an ideal operational amplifier, the output voltage would increase in proportion to increases in the input voltage. In practice, its performance is not quite linear.

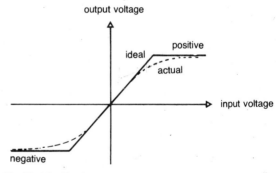

Fig 12.14   Performance of operational amplifier (actual and ideal)

When a certain input voltage is reached, there will be no further rise in the output voltage, and the amplifier is then said to be 'saturated'.

Using the 741 Op Amp as a Differential Amplifier

You will recall that the amplifier voltage gain is the change in output voltage divided by the change in input voltage.

133

$$A_V = \frac{\text{change in output voltage}}{\text{change in input voltage}}.$$

When the 741 Op Amp is connected in a circuit with no external feedback resistors, as shown in Fig 12.15, the voltage gain is high, about 10 000. This is called the **open-loop gain**.

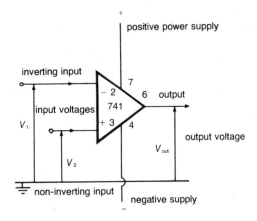

Fig 12.15   Connections to 741 Op Amp.

The input and output voltages to the operational amplifier are measured with respect to an earth or ground rail. There are two inputs to the 741 Op Amp: these are called the **inverting input** and the **non-inverting input**. When both inputs are used, a differential connection is made to the Op Amp. It is the voltage difference $(V_2 - V_1)$ between the input terminals which is amplified and appears as an output voltage. So the output voltage is given by

$V_{out} = A(V_2 - V_1)$ where A is the open-loop gain.

Since a differential input connection is being made to the Op Amp, it is functioning as a **differential amplifier**.

Example
The open-loop gain of a 741 Op Amp is 10 000. If $V_2 = 5.1$ mV and V_1 is 5 mV, what is the output voltage V_{out}?

$$\begin{aligned} V_{out} &= A(V_2 - V_1) \\ &= 10\ 000\ (5.1 - 5)\ \text{mV} \\ &= 10\ 000 \times 0.1\ \text{mV} \\ &= 1\ \text{V}. \end{aligned}$$

The output voltage is 1 V.

■ Design Problems Using the 741 Op Amp

Problem
Design a method of measuring the rotational velocity of a shaft. The rotating shaft is part of an anemometer project that a pupil is making. The aim of the project is to measure the speed of wind by recording the rotational velocity (in revs/min) of a rotating shaft which is driven by the force of the wind on three cups (see Fig 12.16).

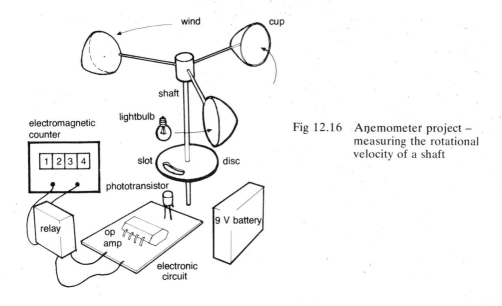

Fig 12.16   Anemometer project –
measuring the rotational
velocity of a shaft

Development

An anemometer project uses three rotating cups to detect the movement of the wind. The cups are attached to a central shaft which will turn when the wind blows. A sensitive photoswitch circuit is required to count the revolutions of the shaft. A disc with a slot in it is fixed to the anemometer shaft (see Fig 12.16). The disc will interrupt a light beam from a lightbulb placed above it. A light-sensitive transducer, such as a phototransistor or a photocell (LDR) is used to detect the interrupted light beam. The signal from the photo transducer can be amplified by an operational amplifier to switch a relay which can activate an electromagnetic counter.

Solutions

One solution to the problem of measuring wind speed is shown in a block diagram form in Fig 12.17.

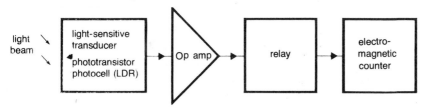

Fig 12.17   Block diagram of solution to anemometer counting system

The phototransistor used in this electronic course is a special kind of *n-p-n* transistor. A **phototransistor** is a transistor with a collector/base junction that is sensitive to the light falling on it. In the top of the phototransistor can is a small lens which focuses light on to the silicon chip inside (see Fig 12.18*a*).

The light falling on the phototransistor controls the electrons crossing the collector/base junction. Variations in light intensity control the base current of the phototransistor. As the light intensity is increased, the base current increases. When the base current increases, the collector current will increase, and the potential difference across the collector/emitter junction will fall. The phototransistor can be used with a 741 Op Amp to produce a suitable light-sensitive switching circuit. The output from the 741 Op Amp can be connected through a resistor to the base of a medium current transistor which can operate a relay. The relay can be used to switch an electromagnetic counter. When the light beam falling on the phototransistor is interrupted, the electromagnetic counter will count one pulse (see Fig 12.19).

Fig 12.18 (a) Phototransistor (MRD3051)

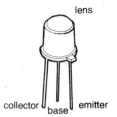

(b) Underside view of MRD3051 phototransistor

(c) Circuit diagram symbol for phototransistor

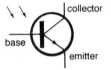

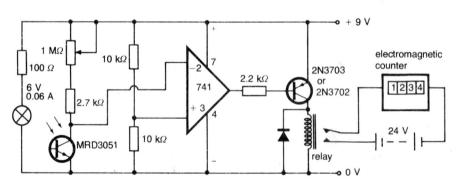

Fig 12.19   Phototransistor/Op Amp counting circuit

An alternative method of solving the problem of counting the revolutions of the anemometer shaft is to use a light-dependent resistor (LDR) instead of a phototransistor. A solution using an LDR is shown in Fig 12.20.

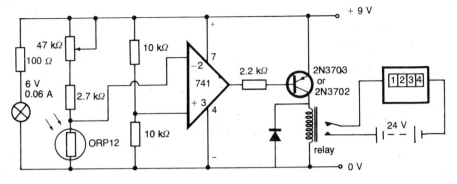

Fig 12.20   Photoswitch/counting circuit using LDR and Op Amp

■ Construction Details

Circuits that require the use of an integrated circuit, such as the 741 Op Amp, are best built on copper-strip matrix board. A commercial make of copper-strip matrix board is called Veroboard. This is a synthetic resin-bonded paper (srbp) board, clad with copper strips (see Fig 12.21). The copper-strip board is drilled with a matrix of holes (0.04″ diameter).

It can be obtained with 0.1″ pitch holes or 0.15″ pitch holes. For use with 741 Op Amps, we will use the 0.1″ pitch matrix copper-strip board.

Fig 12.21   Copper strip matrix board (Veroboard)

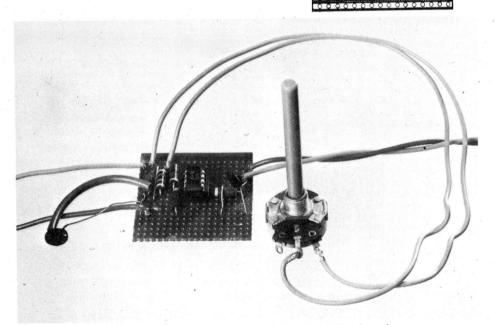

Fig 12.22   Electronic components mounted on plain side of Veroboard

137

The copper strips act as conductors like the tinned copper wire in the conventional circuits previously built with terminal pins and matrix board. The electronic components are mounted on the plain side of the Veroboard, at right angles to the direction of the copper strips (see Fig 12.22). Circuit layouts are designed by electronic components 'bridging' the copper strips.

The electronic component leads are soldered to the copper strips on the reverse side of the board. It is a good idea to clean the copper oxide off the copper strips before soldering by gently rubbing the surface with fine glass paper (not emery cloth or wire wool). This ensures that the solder flows on to the copper strip surface, making a clean soldered joint. Care should be taken to keep the soldered joints small, so that the solder does not bridge the copper strips and cause short-circuiting (see Fig 12.23).

Breaks can be made in the copper strip by the use of a Verocutter (see Fig 12.24) or a small drill.

Twisting the Verocutter or a small drill will produce clean cuts through the copper strip as shown in Fig 12.25.

Fig 12.23   Copper strip side of Veroboard with components soldered to strips

Fig 12.24   Verocutter used to make breaks in copper strip

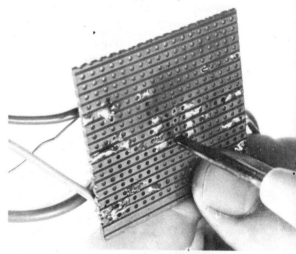

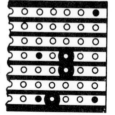

Fig 12.25   Breaks in copper strip of Veroboard

When building a circuit on Veroboard, it is suggested that you begin by soldering the 741 Op Amp in position, near the centre of the Veroboard. The pins of the dual-in-line Op Amp will match the spacing of holes on the Veroboard. The Op Amp must be positioned at right angles to the direction of the copper strips. When all eight pins are soldered, the copper strips can be cut with the Verocutter. Breaks are made between the two rows of Op Amp pins (see Fig 12.24).

Electronic components, such as resistors and capacitors, can be mounted vertically or horizontally on the plain side of the Veroboard (see Fig 12.26).

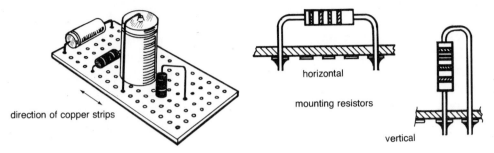

direction of copper strips

horizontal

mounting resistors

vertical

Fig 12.26   Vertical or horizontal mounting of electronic components

The position of electronic components is often located by the use of co-ordinates. The copper strips are numbered (see Fig 12.27). The rows of holes are lettered. A hole can then be located by referring to it by a number and letter, for example, hole D6 in Fig 12.27.

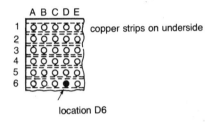

location D6

Fig 12.27   Locating a hole in Veroboard using co-ordinates

You will have an opportunity to use this system in the practical work for this Section.

ADDITIONAL NOTES

Using a Feedback Resistor with the Operational Amplifier

When the 741 Op Amp is used as a straightforward amplifier, as shown in Fig 12.28, it has two inputs and an output. With no external resistors connected to the Op Amp, it is said to operate on **open loop**. The voltage gain of the 741 Op Amp on open loop is high, about 10 000. Operating on open loop, the Op Amp performance is not stable. For some applications, it is essential that the Op Amp is stable, that it performs as a linear amplifier, and that its voltage gain can be accurately controlled. The overall voltage gain is reduced by the use of a feedback resistor (see Fig 12.29).

Fig 12.28 741 Op Amp used as a straightforward amplifier

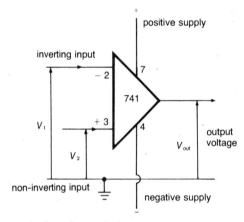

Fig 12.29 Feedback resistor

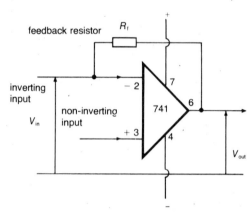

A fraction of the output voltage is fed back through this resistor to the negative input terminal. This is called **negative feedback**. The voltage gain of the operational amplifier is modified by negative feedback. The Op Amp is now said to operate on **closed-loop** amplification.

The Op Amp has two inputs: an inverting input and a non-inverting input. If the non-inverting input terminal is connected to earth, as shown in Fig. 12.30, when an input signal is applied to the inverting input terminal, an increasing positive voltage at the input becomes an increasing negative voltage at the output. The behaviour is sometimes called **phase inversion**. This explains why pin 2 of the 741 Op Amp has a minus sign against it.

Fig 12.30 741 Op Amp as an inverting amplifier

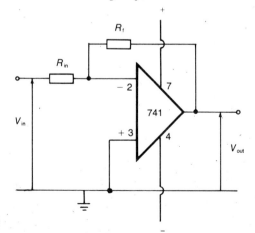

140

The voltage gain of the Op Amp as an inverting amplifier has a negative sign. The voltage gain of an inverting amplifier is given as

$$\text{voltage gain } A_V = \frac{-R_f}{R_{in}}.$$

It can be shown that the voltage gain of the Op Amp can be determined by the values of the input resistor R_{in} and the feedback resistor R_f. Table 1 shows how closed-loop voltage can be determined by selection of input resistor and feedback resistor.

Table 1

Voltage gain A_V	Feedback resistor R_f	Input resistor R_{in}
1	10 kΩ	10 kΩ
10	10 kΩ	1 kΩ
100	100 kΩ	1 kΩ
1000	100 kΩ	100 Ω

When the 741 Op Amp is used as an inverting amplifier or a non-inverting amplifier, it requires a dual power supply. This can be achieved by two batteries as shown in Fig 12.31. Common input and output voltages are measured with respect to earth. The centre tapping of the power supply is connected to earth. The maximum power supply to a 741 Op Amp is ± 18 V.

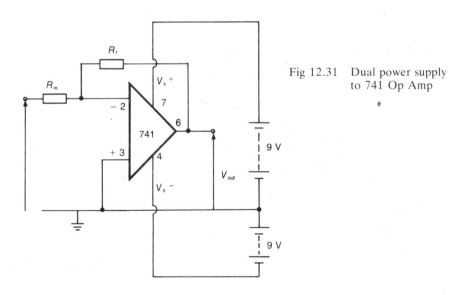

Fig 12.31   Dual power supply to 741 Op Amp

The 741 Op Amp can also be used as a non-inverting amplifier. This is shown in Fig 12.32. The inverting input terminal is connected to earth. When

141

a signal is applied to the non-inverting input, the output signal is **in phase**. That is to say, if the input signal was an increasing positive voltage, the output would be an increasing positive voltage.

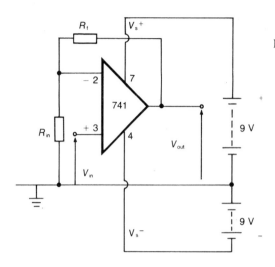

Fig 12.32   741 Op Amp as a
non-inverting amplifier

Table 2

Voltage gain A_V	Input resistor R_{in}	Feedback resistor R_f
10	1 kΩ	9.1 kΩ
100	100 Ω	10 kΩ
1000	100 Ω	100 kΩ